Mozart

1791

*To celebrate
the Bicentennial of Mozart's death with you
the Pavillons Christofle are happy
to present you with this unique work,
a mirror to a shared emotion.*

1991

Pavillon
Christofle

EDITIONS ATLAS

1991

THE YEAR OF MOZART

A YEAR OF MUSICAL EMOTION

On December 5, 1791, Wolfgang Amadeus Mozart, aged 35, passed away leaving a tremendous collection of works as his offering to the whole world.

Through his genius both universal and timeless :

Universal genius through his opera and through the range of styles that he adopted.

Timeless genius, as shown by the immense success of Amadeus, *the Milos Forman film.*
Mozart is still, two centuries after his death, the most popular, the most topical of composers.

This book is the culmination of the talent of the greatest Mozart scholars. Presented as an appointment diary, it is a focus on the various tributes paid to Mozart in 1991 worldwide and on the history of the 18th century.
If it is natural to « love » Mozart, it is fantastic to be able to « live » with Mozart throughout the entire year of the Bicentennial of his death.

With this list of the international events per city, country, by date and exact venue for each one, we are offering you the unique and exclusive program of tributes to Wolfgang Amadeus Mozart by Christofle.

THE MOZART YEAR IN
FRANCE

DATE		VENUE	TELEPHONE	EVENT
PARIS*				
15/4	20h30	Champs-Élysées Theater (1) 47 20 36 37		Serenata notturna, Salzburg Symphony Nº 3, Divertimenti Nºs 7 and 17
15/4	20h30	Gaveau Concert Hall (1) 49 53 05 07		2 Duets for 2 horns, 2 Quartets for flute, Quartet for oboe, Duet for bassoon and violoncello, Quintet for horn
16/4	18h30	Champs-Élysées Theater		Trios K 254, 442, "Les Quilles Trio"
17/4	10h30	Theater of the Grévin Museum (1) 45 44 45 43		Musical: Mozart E…
27-29/4	20h30	Opéra Bastille, amphithéâtre		The Theatre Director, Zaide
30/4	18h30	Champs-Élysées Theater		Sinfonia concertante K 364, Violin Concerto Nº 1
7/5	18h30	Champs-Élysées Theater		Concerto for flute and harp K 299, Sinfonia concertante K 297 b
16/5	20h30	Gaveau Concert Hall		Piano recital
17/5	20h30	Gaveau Concert Hall		Paris Opera Chamber Music Ensemble
23/5	21h	Saint-Louis des Invalides Church (1) 45 55 37 65		Clarinet Concerto, Waisenhausmesse
23-26- 28-31/5-2/6		Châtelet Theater (1) 40 28 28 40		The Abduction from the Seraglio
27/5	20h30	Châtelet Theater		Mitridate
30/5	20h30	Châtelet Theater		Thamos, King of Egypt, Mass in C minor
11/6	19h30	Garnier Opera House (1) 47 42 53 71		La Betulia Liberata
11/6	20h30	Gaveau Concert Hall (1) 43 43 96 96		"Mozart and Rossini" Concert
12/6	20h30	Sainte-Clotilde Basilica (1) 45 44 45 43		Requiem, Grabmusik, Funeral Ode
14/6	20h30	Gaveau Concert Hall		Paris Opera Chamber Music Ensemble
20/6	20h30	Gaveau Concert Hall		Piano recital
27-29/6	19h30	Theater of the Grévin Museum		The Magic Flute
29/6		Notre-Dame Cathedral (1) 43 26 07 39		Coronation Mass
1-3-5-9-11-13-15 17-19/7		Theater of the Grévin Museum		The Magic Flute
13-14/9	20h30	Saint-Eustache Church (1) 42 36 31 05		Requiem
14/9		Sainte-Clotilde Basilica (1) 47 05 22 46		Requiem
24/9	20h30	La Madeleine Church (1) 45 44 45 43		Requiem; Pleyel: Requiem
26-28-29/9		Pleyel Concert Hall		La finta giardiniera (concert version)
2/10	20h30	Châtelet Theater (1) 40 28 28 40		Piano Concerto No.25
4/10	20h30	Maison de Radio-France, Grand Auditorium (1) 42 30 22 22		Piano Concerto No.19
15/10	20h30	Saint-Louis des Invalides Church (1) 45 44 45 43		Davidde Penitente, Clarinet Conerto
29/10	20h30	Saint-Germain-des-Prés Church		Short religious pieces, Mass in C K 139
from 12/11/91 to 16/2/92		Carnavalet Museum (1) 42 72 21 13		Exhibition: "Mozart's sojourns in Paris"
19/11	20h30	Sorbonne, Grand Amphithéâtre (1) 45 44 45 43		The entire Masonic Cantatas for male-voice choirs, Violin Concerto No.3
24/11 or 8/12		Pleyel Concert Hall (1) 45 61 06 30		Mozart Concert
December		Notre-Dame Cathedral (1) 43 26 07 39		Coronation Mass
1/12	19h	Châtelet Theater, Auditorium (1) 40 28 28 40		Divertimenti K 439 b1, b2, b3, Arias from The Marriage of Figaro for 3 basset horns, 4 arias from La Clemenza di Tito for 3 basset horns
4/12		Bastille Opera House (1) 42 78 28 68		Special Gala Evening for the anniversary of Mozart's death (program being finalised)
5/12	20h30	Châtelet Theater		Piano Concerto No27, Reger: Variations on a Mozart theme Messiaen: A Smile
5/12	20h30	Saint-Eustache Church (1) 42 36 31 05		Requiem
10/12	20h30	Saint-Jacques-du-Haut-Pas Church (1) 45 44 45 43		Te Deum, Coronation Mass, Regina Coeli, Jubilate Deo
13/12	20h30	Maison de Radio-France, Grand Auditorium (1) 42 30 22 22		"Jeune homme" Piano Concerto No.9, "Haffner" Symphony No.35
18/12	20h30	Maison de Radio-France, Grand Auditorium		Sinfonia concertante for violin, viola and orchestra
23/12	20h30	Châtelet Theater		Mass in C minor, Messiaen: Small Liturgies

DATE	VENUE	TELEPHONE	EVENT
AULNAY-SOUS-BOIS			
15,17/5	Saint-Sulpice Church (1) 48 66 64 72		La Betulia Liberata
11-13	City Theater		
14-16/6	(1) 48 68 00 22		Play: "Mozart's Magical Nights"
LA CELLE-SAINT-CLOUD			
19/10	City Theater (1) 39 69 20 00		Quartet K 465, Piano Quartets
CERNAY-LA-VILLE			
31/5 20h30	Vaux-de-Cernay Abbey Salle des Moines (1) 45 44 45 43		Requiem, Grabmusik, Funeral Ode
21-22-23-27-28-29/6	Ruins of the Vaux-de-Cernay Abbey (1) 45 44 45 43		The Magic Flute (original version in German)
27-28/9 21h	Pond near the Vaux-de-Cernay Abbey (1) 45 44 45 43		Waterside concerts with fire-works; cassations; Handel: Water Music
13/10 17h	Vaux-de-Cernay Abbey Salle des Moines (1) 45 44 45 43		Symphony Nº.1, Bastien et Bastienne (overture), Piano Concerto Nº.12
VERSAILLES*			
May-June	Saint-Louis Cathedral (1) 39 50 40 65		Mozart Concert (Festival of Versailles)
6/6 20h30	Royal Opera House of the Château de Versailles (1) 42 78 28 68		Mozart Concert
14-15/9	Royal Chapel or Royal Opera House (1) 39 49 48 24		La finta semplice
15/9	Domaine de Versailles (1) 42 67 36 47		Open Day
AIX-EN-PROVENCE			
April	Grand Théâtre 42 38 44 71		Salzburg Symphonies, Serenade in G major, Adagio and fugue for strings, Divertimento for strings and 2 horns
10/7 to 2/8	Saint-Sauveur Cathedral 2 23 45 65		AIX FESTIVAL: Davidde Penitente, Mass in C minor
	Théâtre de l'Archevêché 42 26 02 93		Teresa Berganza Recital
	Hôtel Maynier-d'Oppède 42 63 06 75		Concert arias for soprano
	Saint-Sauveur Cloister and		20 concerts and recitals
	Hôtel Maynier-d'Oppède 42 63 06 75		Bicentenary Special: street dancing and quadrilles, operas, characters in costumes, acrobats
	Cour de l'Archevêché 42 26 02 93		Free concert
ALENÇON			
17/5 18h	Salle Baudelaire 33 26 11 36**		Musiconference by the Friends of Music: "The Life of Mozart"
24/5 20h45	Saint-Léonard Church 33 26 1 36**		Alençon Chamber Orchestra
30/5 20h30	C.D.C. 33 26 11 26**		Instrumental Ensemble of Basse-Normandie
15/6 14h30	Salle Baudelaire 33 26 11 36**		Musiconference by the Friends of Music: "Mozart the Lyricist"
ANGOULEME			
22,23/5 21h	Cathedral 45 95 20 38		Mass in C minor
AVIGNON			
6/6 20h30	90 82 65 11*		Davidde Penitente, Exsultate Jubilate
1-4-7/12	90 82 65 11**		The Magic Flute
BORDEAUX			
17 to 26/5			"MAY IN BORDEAUX", devoted exclusively to Mozart

* PAVILLONS CHRISTOFLE : PARIS : 9 rue Royale 75008 – 24 rue de la Paix 75002 – 95 rue de Passy 75016 – 17 rue de Sèvres 75006
2 Pl. Abbé de Porcaro 78100 Saint-Germain-en-Laye – 40 rue de la Paroisse 78000 Versailles

** TOURIST OFFICE

DATE	VENUE	TELEPHONE	EVENT
22-23-24 25-26/5	Port de la lune Theater 56 91 99 44		Così Fan Tutte
CAEN*			
25-26/5 21h	Notre Dame-de-la Gloriette 31 30 76 20		Requiem, "Linz" Symphony Nº.36
18/6 21h	Salle de l'Échiquier 31 86 27 65**		Serenade Nº.12, Gran Partita
21/6 21h	Salle de l'Échiquier		3 Divertimenti
29/6 21h	Grand Auditorium 31 86 42 00		The Marriage of Figaro (overture), "Prague" Symphony Nº.38
9/7 21h	Salle de l'Échiquier		Arias from operas (transcription), Divertimento K 196, Serenade Nº.11
COLLIOURE			
12/7	Royal Castle 68 82 06 43		The Marriage of Figaro
DIJON			
Summer Music	(planned) 80 43 42 12**		Don Giovanni or The Magic Flute, Pianoforte recital, Clarinet Quintet 3 Concerti (harp, flute and clarinet), Mass in C minor, Amsterdam Puppets.
ÉVIAN			
9 to 19/5	Casino		MUSIC FESTIVAL:
11/5	50 75 04 26*		Sinfonia concertante K 364, Symphony Nº.29
7 to 12/5	50 75 04 26**		Competition for string quartets, devoted exclusively to Mozart
GRENOBLE			
16,17/4 20h30	Theater 76 54 08 37		Così Fan Tutte
19/4 20h30	Salle Dauphiné		Piano Concerto Nº19 ; Haydn
LILLE*			
31/5 20h30	Opera House		
4-6-8/6 20h30	20 30 81 00**		Don Giovanni
2/6 16h			
5/6 and 7/12	20 54 67 00		Requiem
LYON			
15/5 to 15/6 (15 performances)	Opéra House 78 28 09 60		Apollo et Hyacinthus
June/July	Maurice Ravel Auditorium		2nd Mozart "Symphonic Evening"
METZ			
24/4 20h30	L'Arsenal 87 74 16 16		Sinfonia concertante for violin and viola
22/5 20h30	L'Arsenal		"Paris" Symphony Nº.31, Symphony Nº.40
MONTE-CARLO*			
23-26/4 18h30	Le Sporting movie theater 93 30 81 08		The Marriage of Figaro (film)
MONTIGNAC			
20 to 30/7	53 51 82 60**		Périgord Noir Musical Festival Concerts on the theme : "The Italian in Mozart: from Monteverdi to Mozart"
4 to 18/8	53 51 82 60**		Concerts: The Clarinet in Mozart's work and that of his contemporaries
MONTPELLIER			
15,17/-19-21-23/5	Opéra Comédie 67 66 31 11		The Magic Flute
July/August	67 58 67 58**		Radio-France and Montpellier Festival
27/10-3/11	Opera House 67 61 67 61		The Abduction from the Seraglio

** TOURIST OFFICE

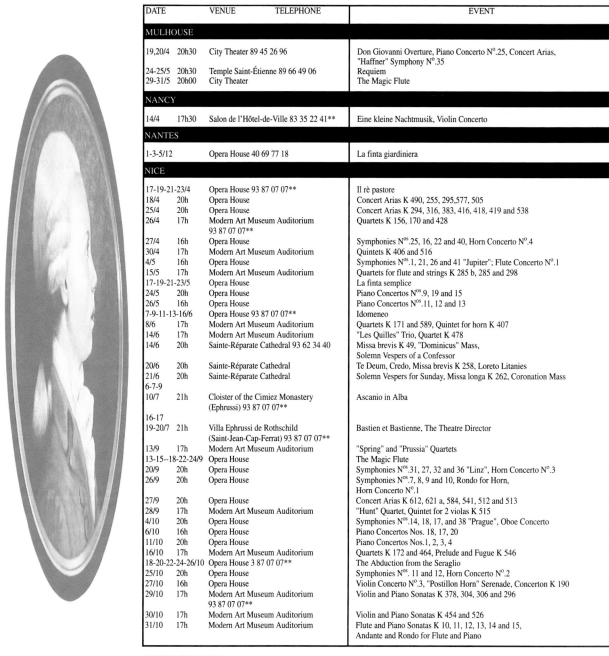

DATE	VENUE	TELEPHONE	EVENT
MULHOUSE			
19,20/4 20h30	City Theater	89 45 26 96	Don Giovanni Overture, Piano Concerto N°.25, Concert Arias, "Haffner" Symphony N°.35
24-25/5 20h30	Temple Saint-Étienne	89 66 49 06	Requiem
29-31/5 20h00	City Theater		The Magic Flute
NANCY			
14/4 17h30	Salon de l'Hôtel-de-Ville	83 35 22 41**	Eine kleine Nachtmusik, Violin Concerto
NANTES			
1-3-5/12	Opera House	40 69 77 18	La finta giardiniera
NICE			
17-19-21-23/4	Opera House	93 87 07 07**	Il rè pastore
18/4 20h	Opera House		Concert Arias K 490, 255, 295,577, 505
25/4 20h	Opera House		Concert Arias K 294, 316, 383, 416, 418, 419 and 538
26/4 17h	Modern Art Museum Auditorium	93 87 07 07**	Quartets K 156, 170 and 428
27/4 16h	Opera House		Symphonies N°s.25, 16, 22 and 40, Horn Concerto N°.4
30/4 17h	Modern Art Museum Auditorium		Quintets K 406 and 516
4/5 16h	Opera House		Symphonies N°s.1, 21, 26 and 41 "Jupiter"; Flute Concerto N°.1
15/5 17h	Modern Art Museum Auditorium		Quartets for flute and strings K 285 b, 285 and 298
17-19-21-23/5	Opera House		La finta semplice
24/5 20h	Opera House		Piano Concertos N°s.9, 19 and 15
26/5 16h	Opera House		Piano Concertos N°s.11, 12 and 13
7-9-11-13-16/6	Opera House	93 87 07 07**	Idomeneo
8/6 17h	Modern Art Museum Auditorium		Quartets K 171 and 589, Quintet for horn K 407
14/6 17h	Modern Art Museum Auditorium		"Les Quilles" Trio, Quartet K 478
14/6 20h	Sainte-Réparate Cathedral	93 62 34 40	Missa brevis K 49, "Dominicus" Mass, Solemn Vespers of a Confessor
20/6 20h	Sainte-Réparate Cathedral		Te Deum, Credo, Missa brevis K 258, Loreto Litanies
21/6 20h	Sainte-Réparate Cathedral		Solemn Vespers for Sunday, Missa longa K 262, Coronation Mass
6-7-9 10/7 21h	Cloister of the Cimiez Monastery (Ephrussi)	93 87 07 07**	Ascanio in Alba
16-17 19-20/7 21h	Villa Ephrussi de Rothschild (Saint-Jean-Cap-Ferrat)	93 87 07 07**	Bastien et Bastienne, The Theatre Director
13/9 17h	Modern Art Museum Auditorium		"Spring" and "Prussia" Quartets
13-15--18-22-24/9	Opera House		The Magic Flute
20/9 20h	Opera House		Symphonies N°s.31, 27, 32 and 36 "Linz", Horn Concerto N°.3
26/9 20h	Opera House		Symphonies N°s.7, 8, 9 and 10, Rondo for Horn, Horn Concerto N°.1
27/9 20h	Opera House		Concert Arias K 612, 621 a, 584, 541, 512 and 513
28/9 17h	Modern Art Museum Auditorium		"Hunt" Quartet, Quintet for 2 violas K 515
4/10 20h	Opera House		Symphonies N°s.14, 18, 17, and 38 "Prague", Oboe Concerto
6/10 16h	Opera House		Piano Concertos Nos. 18, 17, 20
11/10 20h	Opera House		Piano Concertos Nos.1, 2, 3, 4
16/10 17h	Modern Art Museum Auditorium		Quartets K 172 and 464, Prelude and Fugue K 546
18-20-22-24-26/10	Opera House	3 87 07 07**	The Abduction from the Seraglio
25/10 20h	Opera House		Symphonies N°s. 11 and 12, Horn Concerto N°.2
27/10 16h	Opera House		Violin Concerto N°.3, "Postillon Horn" Serenade, Concerton K 190
29/10 17h	Modern Art Museum Auditorium	93 87 07 07**	Violin and Piano Sonatas K 378, 304, 306 and 296
30/10 17h	Modern Art Museum Auditorium		Violin and Piano Sonatas K 454 and 526
31/10 17h	Modern Art Museum Auditorium		Flute and Piano Sonatas K 10, 11, 12, 13, 14 and 15, Andante and Rondo for Flute and Piano

** TOURIST OFFICE

THE MOZART YEAR IN GERMANY

DATE	VENUE	TELEPHONE	EVENT
3/11 17h	Modern Art Museum Auditorium		Violin and Piano Sonatas K 13, 14, and 15, Trios K 572 and 548
10-12-14-16/11	Opera House		La Clemenza di Tito
17/11 16h	Opera House		Violin Concertos N°s.5 and 7, A Musical Joke
23/11 16h	Opera House		Sinfonia concertante for Violin and Viola K 364, "Haffner" Serenade K 250
28/11 20h	Opera House		Piano Concertos N°s. 25 and 26, Rondo K 386
30/11 16h	Opera House		Piano Concertos N°s. 5, 6 and 8
5/12 20h	Acropolis, salle Apollon 93 92 83 00		Requiem, Concerto for 2 pianos K 365
7/12 17h	Modern Art Museum Auditorium		Quartets K 173 and 465, Clarinet Quintet K 581
20/12 20h	Opera House		Pianos Concertos N°s. 22 and 24
21-22-24-25-27-28-29-31/12	Opera House		The Marriage of Figaro

STRASBOURG*

18/4 20h30	Palais des Congrès, Salle Érasme 88 32 43 10		Salzburg Symphony N°.2, Eine kleine Nachtmusik, Divertimento for strings, 2 horns and bassoon, Serenata notturna
10-12-16-18/5118/5 4-6-9-11/6	City Hall 88 75 48 00		The Magic Flute
3/6 20h30	Conservatoire 88 36 55 02		Recital-Conference: "Mozart on the Pianoforte"
7/6 to 6/7			53RD FESTIVAL OF MUSIC
7/6	Cathedral 88 32 75 78		Requiem
8/6	88 32 43 10		Mozart and Brahms (Royal Philharmonic Orchestra)
12/6	88 32 43 10		"Jupiter" Symphony N°.41
19/6	88 32 43 10		Song Recital
20/6			Handel's Messiah, Mozart's version
27-29/6-2/7	88 32 43 10		The Marriage of Figaro
28/6	88 32 43 10		Flute Concerto N°.2, Clarinet Concerto
6/7	Ebersmunster Abbey 88 85 70 12		Solemn Vespers of a Confessor, Mass in C minor
14 to16/10	(1) 42 78 28 68 (Comité National Mozart)		International Congress: "Communication in Europe in Mozart's time""
14-17/10	Palais des Congrès		The Marriage of Figaro
15/10	Rohan Castle 88 38 73 43		Music for glass harmonica by Mozart
January 92	88 37 67 68**		Festival of music in tribute to Mozart

AUGSBURG

4-11/5 19h30	Kleiner Goldener Saal		L'Oca del Cairo and other opera extracts
5/5 11h	Zeughaus, Hollsaal		
7-/5 19h	Zeughaus, Hollsaal		Conferences: "Mozart Yesterday and Today" (series)
14/5 19h	Neue Universität, Amphi I		
5-7/5 20h	Kongreßhalle		Eine kleine Nachtmusik; Bassoon Concerto; "Jupiter" Symphony N°.41
9-10-11-12/5	Spielküche Theatre		Play: "The Prodigy Child" (by Mary Hall-Surface)
9/5 17h	Herrgottsruh Church		Sonata da Chiesa K 278; Symphony N°.33; Maurerische Trauermusik K 477; Litany K 243
11-12/5 18h	Mozarthaus		Works for violin and piano
15-17-29-30/6	(821) 308 77		The complete works for violin and piano
12/5 11h	Mozarthaus		Works for violin and piano
12-16-24/5-	Kongreßalle		Don Giovanni
20/5 20h	Kleiner Goldener Saal		Chamber music concert and conference
20-26/5	Haus St Ulrich		Concert: 16th Week of Mozart Music (any musician can take part)
2/6 17h	Barfüßer Church		Organ concert
2/6 19h	Kongreßalle		Don Giovanni
8-9/6 20h	Spielküche Theatre		Play: "The Prodigy Child" (by Mary Hall-Surface)
8-9-15-16/6	St Ulrich and Afra Basilica and Protestant Church		Days of Organ Music

* PAVILLONS CHRISTOFLE FRANCE : 45 Bd Paoli 20200 BASTIA – 35 rue St. Pierre 14000 CAEN
52 rue de la Grande Chaussée 59800 LILLE – 42 Bd des Moulins 98000 MONTE CARLO
5 rue Lafayette 35000 RENNES – 44 rue des Hallebardes 67000 STRASBOURG

** TOURIST OFFICE

DATE		VENUE	TELEPHONE	EVENT
11/6	19h	Neue Universität, Amphi I		Conferences: "Mozart Yesterday and Today" (series)
25/6		Zeughaus, Hollsaal		
15-16-17-29-30/6-		Mozarthaus		Works for violin and piano
23/6	17h	St Paul		Church Sonatas
2-16/7	19h	Neue Universität, Amphi I		Conferences: "Mozart Yesterday and Today" (series)
6/7	19h	Kongreßvhalle		Nocturnes K 436, 438, 549; Te Deum K 141
7/7	17h	Barfüßer Church		"Tribute to Mozart": Compositions on Mozart themes
11-12-13-14/7		Spielküche Theatre		Theatre: "The Prodigy Child"
2-6-11-14/7		Schaezlerpalais		4 chamber music concerts
4/8	20h	Schaezlerpalais Rococo Hall		Works for 2 pianos, works for piano for 4 hands
22 to 29/9				40TH GERMAN MOZART FESTIVAL
22/9	11h11	Goldener Saal des Rathauses		Overture - Masonic Cantata - "Laut verkünde unsere Freude" K 623 - "Mozart through his correspondence"
22/9	20h	Kleiner Goldener Saal		L'oca del Cairo
23/9	20h	Kleiner Goldener Saal		Evening of songs with Maria Venuti
24/9	20h	Schaezlerpalais		Alban Berg Quartet
25/9	20h	Kreuz Church		Requiem
27/9	20h	Kongreßhalle		Nocturne K 286, Clarinet Concerto "Prague" Symphony N°.38
28/9	20h	Schaezlerpalais		Piano Concertos N°s.11 and 13
29/9	20h	Kongreßhalle		Handel's Messiah, Mozart version
14/10	20h	Kleiner Goldener Saal		International Mozart Series: Sinfonia concertante K 364 and other works
26/10	20h	Kleiner Goldener Saal		Sonatas K 310, 576, Fantasia K 397, Variations K 455 Reading of Mozart's correspondence and poems devoted to Mozart
27/10	16h	St Ulrich und Afra Basilica		Short religious pieces
12-19-26/11		Zeughaus, Neue Universität		Conferences: "Mozart yesterday and today"
16/11	15h30	Haus St Ulrich		Seminar on the religious music and the Requiem by Mozart
17/11	19h	City Theatre		The Abduction from the Seraglio
4/12	20h	University Concert Hall		Piano Concerto N°26, Serenade K 388
5/12	20h	Kongreßhalle		Requiem

FOR INFORMATION, PLEASE PHONE (821) 30877

BERLIN

20-21-22-24/4	Philharmonic Kammermusiksaal, West Berlin (30) 261 43 83	Serenade K 375, Piano Concertos N°s 17, 25
28/4	Deutsche Staatsoper, East Berlin (2) 200 47 62	The Abduction from the Seraglio
3/5	Deutsche Staatsoper	Così Fan Tutte
23-24-25-26/5	Philharmonic Kammermusiksaal	Symphonies N°s.40 and 41 "Jupiter"
29/5-1/6	Philharmonic Kammermusiksaal	Nocturne for 4 sextets for horns and strings instruments
14/6	Deutsche Staatsoper	The Marriage of Figaro
16-20-23-26-29/6	Deutsche Oper, West Berlin	La Clemenza di Tito
17-20/6 20h	Philharmonic Kammermusiksaal	Serenade and Piano Concerto
27/6	Deutsche Staatsoper	The Abduction from the Seraglio
8/7	Deutsche Staatsoper	The Marriage of Figaro
21-23/9	Deutsche Staatsoper	Don Giovanni

BONN

13/10	19h	Opera House (228) 72 81	The Magic Flute
1/12	19h	Opera House	Don Giovanni

COLOGNE

1/5	Opera House	The Abduction from the Seraglio
2/6	Opera House	Don Giovanni

THE MOZART YEAR IN
AUSTRIA

DATE	VENUE	TELEPHONE	EVENT
DORTMUND			
24-25/6 20h	Opera House	(231) 14 03 41	Symphonies Nos.25 and 38 "Prague", Horn Concertos Nos. 2 and 3
5/12	Opera House		Don Giovanni (first night)
MUNICH			
April-May	Cuvilliés Theater	(89) 23 911**	Apollo et Hyacinthus; Il sogno di Scipione
5/12	National Theatre		Special concert
STUTTGART			
30/4		(711) 48 10 76**	Piano Concerto No.24
1-3-5-12/5	Theater in the Schwetzinger Castle	(711) 48 10 76	The Abduction from the Seraglio
SALZBURG			
April 19h30	Puppet Theater		Puppet play
April to October (every day)	Mirabell Palace Residenz		Concerts
April to October	Klessheim Palace		Gala evening
20-4 19h	Landestheater		Don Giovanni
20-27/4 20h	Gothic Hall		Serenades
25/4 19h30	Mozarteum		Orchestral concert (Mozarteum)
27/4-3-4-11-12-18-19-24-25-31/5	Landestheater		The Marriage of Figaro
1/5 to 20/10	Hohensalzburg Fortress		Concerts
May to December	Gothic Hall		Serenades
2-9--136-23-30/5	Mozarteum and Grand Auditorium		Orchestral concerts
3/5 19h30	Large Festival Hall		Orchestral concert (Slovenic Philharmonic)
7-8/5 19h30	Large Festival Hall		Orchestral concert (Dresden Philharmonic)
8/5 18h	Cathedral		Solemn Vespers of a Confessor
15/5 to 15/10	Cathedral Museum		Exhibition: "Salzburg in Mozart's Day"
20/5 09h	Franciscan Church		Trinitatis Mass
23/5 19h30	Residenz		Violin and piano Sonatas from Bach to Mozart
26/5 10h	Cathedral		Trinitatis Mass
29/5 10h	Cathedral		Litaniae de venerabili altaris sacramento
End-May Beg-June			150TH ANNIVERSARY OF THE MOZARTEUM ACADEMY
1-8/6 19h	Landestheater		The Marriage of Figaro
5-6/6 19h30	Large Festival Hall		Hungarian Philharmonic Orchestra and Choirs
6-13-20-27/6-	Mozarteum		Camerata Academica and Choirs
7/6 19h30	Large Festival Hall		Mozarteum
15-16-22-23-29-30/6	Hellbrunn Castle		"Tribute to Mozart"
23/6 10h	Cathedral		Missa brevis K 192
July to September	Rupertinum		Exhibition: "The historical Mozart series"
July to September	St Gilgen		Organ Concerts
14/7 10h	Cathedral		Missa brevis K 115
24/7 20h30	Franciscan Church		Organ concert
26/7 to 31/8			SALZBURG FESTIVAL:
	Large Festival Hall		The Magic Flute, The Marriage of Figaro
	Small Festival Hall		Così Fan Tutte, The Abduction from the Seraglio
	Riding School		Idomeneo
1/8 to 20/12	Max-Reinhardt- Gendenkstätte		Exhibition: "Portraits of singers interpreting the works of Mozart"
4-11-15-18-25/8	Franciscan Church		Waisenhausmesse, Missa brevis K 275, Coronation Mass, Missa brevis K 192, Missa solemnis K 337
11-25/8 10h	Cathedral		Missa brevis K 194, Missa solemnis K 337
16-19-23-29/8-	Landestheater		Opera: "Mozart in New York" (by Helmut Eder)
5-12/9 19h	Mozarteum		Camerata Academica
5-12-21-27/9-	Landestheater		Ballet: Bastien et Bastienne, Les Petits Riens

*PAVILLON CHRISTOFLE : GERMANY :   Goethestrasse 29 6000 FRANKFURT - M.1
** TOURIST OFFICE

DATE		VENUE	TELEPHONE	EVENT
15-18/9				Symposium:"Towards a Mozart Future"
27-30/9	19h30	Large Festival Hall		Moscow Radio Symphony Orchestra
3-24/10	19h	Mozarteum		Camerata Academica
3/10	20h	Künstlerhaus		"28 understandings with Mozart" (concert)
5/10	19h	Landestheater		Ballet: Bastien et Bastienne, Les Petits Riens
6/10	09h	Franciscan Church		Missa piccolomini
10/10	19h30	Mozarteum		Vienna Chamber Orchestra
14/10	19h30	Mozarteum		Salzburg Chamber Orchestra
15/10	19h30	Mozarteum		Concert: Soloist from the Mozarteum International Foundation
17/10	19h30	Mozarteum		Munich Chamber Orchestra
17-18-31/10		Large Festival Hall		Salzburg Mozarteum Orchestra
19-20/10	1	Cathedral		Coronation Mass, Dominicus Mass
21-23/10	19h30	Large Festival Hall		Stuttgart Radio Symphony Orchestra
25/10	19h30	Large Festival Hall		Mozarteum Academy Orchestra
28/10	19h30	Great Auditorium		Concert
29/10	19h30	Great Auditorium		Mozart Mass
1/11	9h	Franciscan Church		"Organ Solo" Mass K 259
1-3-8-8-10-15/11-		Landestheater		Così Fan Tutte
2/11	19h	Cathedral		Requiem
3/11	10h	Cathedral		Missa brevis K 49
3/11	20h	Franciscan Church		Requiem
7/11	19h30	Mozarteum		Munich Chamber Orchestra
8/11	19h30	Large Festival Hall		Salzburg Mozarteum Orchestra
14/11	19h30	Mozarteum		Salzburg Mozarteum Orchestra
14-15/11	19h30	Large Festival Hall		Hungarian National Philharmonic Orchestra
21/11	19h	Mozarteum		Camerata Academica
22-24-	19h	Landestheater		The Magic Flute
26-28-30/11				
28/11	19h30	Great Auditorium		Vienna Chamber Orchestra
1-4-6-8-10-12-14-15-17-				
19-21-22-25-28/12		Landestheater		The Magic Flute
2 to 21/12		Gothic Hall		Serenades (pre-Christmas Eine Kleine Nachtmusik)
4/12	20h	St Peter's Church		Requiem
5/12	19h30	Great Auditorium		Munich Chamber Orchestra
8/12	9h	Franciscan Church		Dominicus Mass
8-25-26-29/12		Cathedral		Waisenhausmesse, Credo K 257, Missa piccolomini, Missa brevis K 140
8/12	19h30	Large Festival Hall		Requiem, Symphony Nº. 40
12/12	19h	Great Auditorium		Camerata Academica
19/12	19h30	Mozarteum		Vienna Chamber Orchestra
23-25-29/12		Mozarteum		Christmas Galas: Mozart Serenades
24/12	22h	Franciscan Church		Missa brevis K 49
24/12	23h20	Cathedral		"Organ Solo" Mass K 259
26/12	9h	Franciscan Church		Missa brevis K 194
31/12	17h	Cathedral		Te Deum

FOR INFORMATION, PLEASE PHONE (662) 84 22 96

VIENNA*

DATE		VENUE	TELEPHONE	EVENT
21-28/4	10h	St Michael's Church		Free sacred music concerts
8/4-11/5	Eveng	Staatsoper		The Magic Flute
9/5	19h	Volksoper		The Magic Flute
21/4	19h	Volksoper		Così Fan Tutte
May to October		National Library		"Requiem" Exhibition
5-12-19-26/5		St Michael's Church		Free sacred music concerts
9-11-27/5		Konzerthaus Great Hall		Vienna Philharmonic Orchestra
10-13-16-18/5		Staatsoper		La Clemenza di Tito
11/5	11h	Theater an der Wien		The Marriage of Figaro
12-14/5	Eveng	Staatsoper		Mozart Ballets

DATE		VENUE	TELEPHONE	EVENT
12-14-16-18-				
20-22/5	Eveng	Theater an der Wien		The Marriage of Figaro
13/5	19h30	Konzerthaus Great Hall		Camerata Academica
14/5	19h	Konzerthaus Great Hall		La Clemenza di Tito
15-17-20-23/5		Staatsoper		The Abduction from the Seraglio
16/5	19h30	Konzerthaus Great Hall		Orchestra of the 18th century
16/5	19h	Volksoper		Don Giovanni
19-21-28/5		Staatsoper		The Magic Flute
22-24-26/5		Staatsoper		Lucio Silla
25/29/5	19h30	Konzerthaus Great Hall		Vienna Philharmonic Orchestra
25-27-30/5-3/6		Staatsoper		Idomeneo
27-28/5	19h30	Konzerthaus Mozart Hall		Alban Berg Quartet
29/5-	Eveng	Staatsoper		Mozart ballets
30/5-9-23/6		Volksoper		The Magic Flute
31/5-5/6	19h30	Konzerthaus Great Hall		Piano recital
31/5-2-4-6/6		Theater an der Wien		Don Giovanni
1-4-6/6	Eveng	Staatsoper		Così Fan Tutte
2-9-16-23-30/6		St Michael's Church		Free sacred music concerts
3/6	19h30	Konzerthaus Great Hall		Mass in C minor
7/6	19h30	Musikverein Brahms Hall		Masonic music
8-9/6	19h	Konzerthaus, Great Hall		La finta giardiniera, concert version
9/6	Eveng	Staatsoper		Mozart ballets
11/6	19h30	Konzerthaus Great Hall		Handel's Messiah, Mozart version
12-14/6	Eveng	Theater an der Wien		The Magic Flute
13-24/6	19h	Volksoper		Così Fan Tutte
14/6	19h30	Konzerthaus Great Hall		Vienna Philharmonic Orchestra
16/6	11h	Konzerthaus Great Hall		Europe Chamber Orchestra
23/6	11h	Konzerthaus Great Hall		Vienna Chamber Orchestra
23/6	19h30	Konzerthaus Great Hall		Coronation Mass
1 to 6-11-12-13-15 to 20,				
22-27-29-30-31/7		Schönbrunn Castle Theatre		The Magic Flute
2-11-13-17-25/7		Rathausplatz (Town Hall Sq.)		Opera on film: The Magic Flute (free)
2-3-4-5-11-12-13-18-				
19-20/7-	Eveng	Summer music in Vienna		Piano Concertos
		(place to be decided)		
-				
3-4-16-22-27-30/7		Rathausplatz		Opera on film: Don Giovanni
5/7	Eveng	Rathausplatz		Opera on film: Idomeneo (free)
6-14-19-24/7		Rathausplatz		Opera on film: The Abduction from the Seraglio (free)
7-14-21-28/7		St Michael's Church		Free sacred music concerts
7-12-18-29/7		Rathausplatz (Town Hall Sq.)		Opera on film: Così fan tutte (free)
8-21-31/7	Eveng	Rathausplatz		Opera on film: La Clemenza di Tito (free)
10-23/7	Eveng	Rathausplatz		Opera on film: Mitridate (free)
11-15-18-22-25/7		University Church		La Betulia Liberata
16/7	Eveng	Schönbrunn Castle		Artis Quartet
		Theatre - Gallery		
19-20/7		Wiener Kammeroper		Belvedere Competition
20-26/7	Eveng	Rathausplatz (Town Hall Sq.)		Opera on film: The Marriage of Figaro (free)
23/7	Eveng	Schönbrunn Castle Gallery		Piano recital
1-2-3, 5 to 9, 10-12-13-14-16-17, 19 to 24,				
26 to 31/8-		Schönbrunn Castle Gallery		The Magic Flute
1-13-22-28/8		Rathausplatz (Town Hall Sq.)		Opera on film: The Abduction from the Seraglio (free)
2-3-14-20-21/8		Rathausplatz		Opera on film: Così fan tutte (free)
4-11-18-25/8		St Michael's Church		Free sacred music concerts
4-5-11-17-31/8		Rathausplatz		Opera on film: The Magic Flute (free)
6-26/8	Eveng	Rathausplatz		Opera on film: Mitridate (free)
7-15-16-25-30/8		Rathausplatz		Opera on film: The Marriage of Figaro (free)
8-18-27/8	Eveng	Rathausplatz		Opera on film: La Clemenza di Tito (free)
9-10-23-29/8		Rathausplatz		Opera on film: Don Giovanni (free)

THE MOZART YEAR IN
BELGIUM

THE MOZART YEAR IN
CANADA

DATE	VENUE	TELEPHONE	EVENT
11-14-19-22/8	Schönbrunn Castle Gallery		Artis Quartet
12-19/8 Eveng	Rathausplatz		Opera on film: Idomeneo (free)
1-8-15-22-29/9	St Michael's Church		Free sacred music concerts
2-5-19-27/9	Staatsoper		The Magic Flute
5-26/10 Eveng			
9/9-6/10 19h	Volksoper		Don Giovanni
26-30/9, 12-29/10	Staatsoper		The Marriage of Figaro
6-13-20-27/10	St Michael's Church		Free sacred music concerts
13-15-17-19-20/10	Volksoper		Ballet: "Mozart in Vienna" (Maurice Béjart)
16-17/10 19h30	Konzerthaus Great Hall		Vienna Philharmonic Orchestra
1-17-29/11	Volksoper, Staatsoper		The Magic Flute
3-10-17-24/11-	St Michael's Church		Free sacred music concerts
6-9-15/11 Eveng	Staatsoper		Così Fan Tutte
6-26-28/11	Volksoper		The Marriage of Figaro
18-21/11 19h30	Konzerthaus Mozart Hall		Haydn Trio
22/11 19h30	Konzerthaus Mozart Hall		Piano recital (Murray Perahia)
28/11 Eveng	Staatsoper		Idomeneo
28-29-30/11-1/12	Hofburg Kongresszentrum		Symposium: "Music and Free-masonry from Mozart's time to nowadays"
1-8-15-22-29/12	St Michael Church		Free concerts of sacred music
1-4/12 Eveng	Staatsoper		Idomeneo
1-5-16/1218h	Volksoper		The Magic Flute
3-4/12 19h30	Konzerthaus Mozart Hall		Alban Berg Quartet
4-6/12 19h30	Konzerthaus Great Hall		Vienna Symphony Orchestra
5-6/12 19h30	Musikverein Golden Room		Europe Chamber Orchestra
5 to 9, 12 to 16/12	Herbert Lederers Theatre		"Mozart's correspondence"
5/12 Eveng	Stephansdom		Requiem
9-10-11-12-13/12	Konzerthaus Great Hall		Congress: "Music in education"
14-29/12 19h	Volksoper		The Marriage of Figaro

FOR INFORMATION, PLEASE PHONE (1) 587 98 43

BRUSSELS*

27-28-30/4	Royal Theater of la Monnaie (2) 217 22 11		The Magic Flute
2-3-4-5-7-8-10-11-14-15-17-			
18-19/5 20h	Royal Theater of la Monnaie		The Magic Flute
15/9 20h	Royal Theater of la Monnaie		March K 290; Divertimento K 205; 3 Arias K 612, 469; "Prague" Symphony N°.38
16/9 20h	Royal Theater of la Monnaie		Don Giovanni (concert version)
17-20-22-25-27-			
29-31/12 20h	Royal Theater of la Monnaie		The Marriage of Figaro

MONTREAL*

1/3 to 20/5	Place des Arts (613) 563 14 44		Mozart Exhibition (scores, engravings, etc.)
25/3 20 h	St Jean-Baptiste Church (514) 598 08 70		Requiem
6/7 to 26/8	(514) 769 7190		Mozart Exhibition (scores, engravings, etc.); Orford Festival
Summer	(514) 842 3402		Mozart Plus Festival (Montreal Symphony Orchestra)
5/12	(514) 842 3402		Requiem
27/4 to 3/5/92	Opera House(514) 985 2222		Mozart Festival (Concerts, conferences, operas, etc.)

TORONTO

23/5 to 5/6	Roy Thomson Hall (416) 686 8046		Mozart Exhibition (scores, engravings, etc.)
24/5 20h	Roy Thomson Hall (416) 593 4828		Festival's Opening Concert
25/5 19h	(416) 965 40 08**		Children of the Royal Conservatory of Music
26-27-28-29-31/5	Walter Hall (Toronto University) (416) 978 37 44		Singing Competition (pupils from The Royal Conservatory of Music)
2/6 14h	Roy Thomson Hall		Concerts given by the winners of the competition

* PAVILLONS CHRISTOFLE :   AUSTRIA : Kohlmarkt 18, 1010 VIENNA
BELGIUM : 29 Av. Louise 1050 BRUSSELS

**TOURIST OFFICE

THE MOZART YEAR IN
SPAIN

THE MOZART YEAR IN
THE UNITED
STATES

DATE	VENUE	TELEPHONE	EVENT
30/5 20h	St Paul's Anglican Church (416) 961 81 16		Toronto Orpheus Choral Society
1-4-6-8-10-13-16-20-22/6	Elgin Theater (416) 594 07 55		Così Fan Tutte
5-7-9-11-15-18-21/6	Elgin Theater		La Clemenza di Tito
10 to 15/6	McMillan Theater		"Marvellous Mozart" Ballet
3/6	St Patrick's Church (416) 598 3269		Concert: Elmer Iseler Singers
14-17-19-23-25-27/6	O'Keefe Centre (416) 393 7469		The Marriage of Figaro
15/6 14h-19h30	Imperial oil Opera Theatre		Canadian Children's Opera Chorus
16/6 14h	(416) 363 2348		
17/6	Cinémathèque Ontario (416) 965 4008*		Opera on film: The Magic Flute
18/6 to 23/6			Other operas on film
25/6 20h	Winter Garden (416) 965 4008**		Orford String Quartet
26/6 20h	Winter Garden		Chamber Players of Toronto
28-29/6 20h	Winter Garden		Play: "The Madcap Adventures of Fräulein Mozart"

BARCELONA*

DATE	VENUE	TELEPHONE	EVENT
13/5 21h	Palau de la Musica Catalana (3) 268 10 00		Ascanio in Alba (overture); Piano Concerto N°.15; Gallimathias musicum ; Divertimento K 287
20-23-26-28-30/6-2-4-6/7	Gran Teatro del Liceu (3) 318 91 22		The Magic Flute
2/12 21h	Palau de la Musica Catalana		Special Concert :Thamos, King of Egypt; In Praise of Friendship, Divertimento specially created by 7 great composers

MADRID*

DATE	VENUE	TELEPHONE	EVENT
22/4 to 29/6			4th MADRID MOZART FESTIVAL
22/4	Auditorium (1) 411 40 14		Piano and violin Sonatas (Mozart and Beethoven)
30/4	Auditorium		Symphonies N°s.39 and 41 "Jupiter"; Piano Concerto N°.20
1/5	Auditorium		Mozart and Rossini Arias (Cecilia Bartoli, Mezzo)
1/5	Teatro Salón Cervantes de Alcalá de Henares (1) 882 24 97		The Magic Flute
2,3/5	Teatro Salón Cervantes de Alcalá de Henares		The Marriage of Figaro
4,5/5	Teatro Albéniz (1) 522 02 00		The Magic Flute
7,8/5	Teatro Albéniz		La Clemenza di Tito
9 to 12/5	Real Coliseo Carlos III de El Escorial (1) 890 44 11		Apollo et Hyacinthus
12,13/5	Teatro Albéniz		Bastien et Bastienne
14,15/5	Teatro Albéniz		La finta semplice
16,17/5	Teatro Albéniz		La finta giardiniera
18/5	Real Coliseo Carlos III de El Escorial		La finta semplice
18,19/5	Teatro Albéniz		L'oca del Cairo, Lo sposo deluso, The Theatre Director
24/5	Teatro Salón Cervantes de Alcalá de Henares		Mozart Quartets
31/5	Auditorium		Piano Concerto N°.25, Mass in C minor
4,5,7,8/6	Auditorium		3 great quartets, 3 quintets with viola, quintet for clarinet
18,20/6	Teatro Albéniz		Don Giovanni
22/6	Teatro Salón Cervantes de Alcalá de Henares		Don Giovanni
28/6	Auditorium		Symphonies: "Paris" N°.31, "Linz" N°.36, "Prague" N°.38
29/6	Auditorium		Closing concert: Symphony N°.40, Requiem

BOSTON

DATE	VENUE	TELEPHONE	EVENT
5/29 to 6/9	(Music Festival)		Mass in C minor, Gala concert; The Marriage of Figaro (concert version); Chamber music concerts

CHICAGO*

DATE	VENUE	TELEPHONE	EVENT
5/19	St Paul's Church (312) 935 3800		Choral Ensemble of Chicago: Short religious pieces; cantatas, vocal trios; canons; Thamos, King of Egypt (extracts)

* PAVILLONS CHRISTOFLE   CANADA : Chez Ogilvy 1307 rue Sainte-Catherine Ouest MONTREAL, P.Q. H3G 1P7
SPAIN : 9 carrer de Bori i Fontesta 08021 BARCELONA – Jorge Juan, 4 28001 MADRID

** TOURIST OFFICE

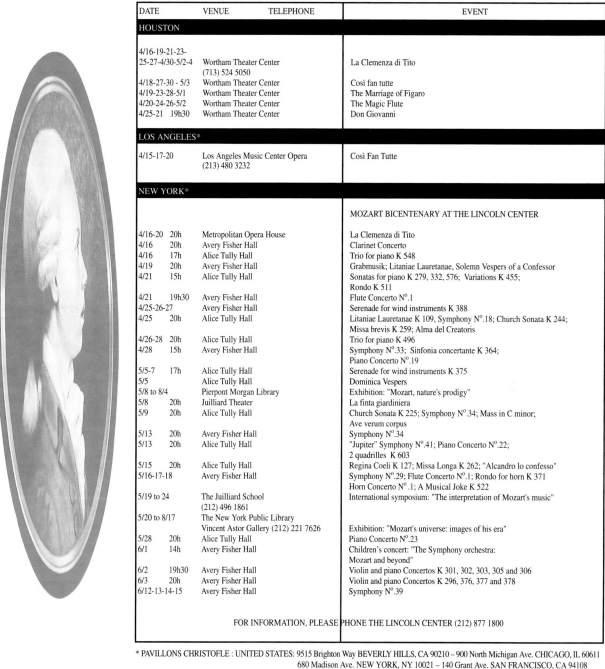

DATE	VENUE	TELEPHONE	EVENT
HOUSTON			
4/16-19-21-23-25-27-4/30-5/2-4	Wortham Theater Center (713) 524 5050		La Clemenza di Tito
4/18-27-30 - 5/3	Wortham Theater Center		Così fan tutte
4/19-23-28-5/1	Wortham Theater Center		The Marriage of Figaro
4/20-24-26-5/2	Wortham Theater Center		The Magic Flute
4/25-21 19h30	Wortham Theater Center		Don Giovanni
LOS ANGELES*			
4/15-17-20	Los Angeles Music Center Opera (213) 480 3232		Così Fan Tutte
NEW YORK*			
			MOZART BICENTENARY AT THE LINCOLN CENTER
4/16-20 20h	Metropolitan Opera House		La Clemenza di Tito
4/16 20h	Avery Fisher Hall		Clarinet Concerto
4/16 17h	Alice Tully Hall		Trio for piano K 548
4/19 20h	Avery Fisher Hall		Grabmusik; Litaniae Lauretanae, Solemn Vespers of a Confessor
4/21 15h	Alice Tully Hall		Sonatas for piano K 279, 332, 576; Variations K 455; Rondo K 511
4/21 19h30	Avery Fisher Hall		Flute Concerto N°.1
4/25-26-27	Avery Fisher Hall		Serenade for wind instruments K 388
4/25 20h	Alice Tully Hall		Litaniae Lauretanae K 109, Symphony N°.18; Church Sonata K 244; Missa brevis K 259; Alma del Creatoris
4/26-28 20h	Alice Tully Hall		Trio for piano K 496
4/28 15h	Avery Fisher Hall		Symphony N°.33; Sinfonia concertante K 364; Piano Concerto N°.19
5/5-7 17h	Alice Tully Hall		Serenade for wind instruments K 375
5/5	Alice Tully Hall		Dominica Vespers
5/8 to 8/4	Pierpont Morgan Library		Exhibition: "Mozart, nature's prodigy"
5/8 20h	Juilliard Theater		La finta giardiniera
5/9 20h	Alice Tully Hall		Church Sonata K 225; Symphony N°.34; Mass in C minor; Ave verum corpus
5/13 20h	Avery Fisher Hall		Symphony N°.34
5/13 20h	Alice Tully Hall		"Jupiter" Symphony N°.41; Piano Concerto N°.22; 2 quadrilles K 603
5/15 20h	Alice Tully Hall		Regina Coeli K 127; Missa Longa K 262; "Alcandro lo confesso"
5/16-17-18	Avery Fisher Hall		Symphony N°.29; Flute Concerto N°.1; Rondo for horn K 371 Horn Concerto N° .1; A Musical Joke K 522
5/19 to 24	The Juilliard School (212) 496 1861		International symposium: "The interpretation of Mozart's music"
5/20 to 8/17	The New York Public Library Vincent Astor Gallery (212) 221 7626		Exhibition: "Mozart's universe: images of his era"
5/28 20h	Alice Tully Hall		Piano Concerto N°.23
6/1 14h	Avery Fisher Hall		Children's concert: "The Symphony orchestra: Mozart and beyond"
6/2 19h30	Avery Fisher Hall		Violin and piano Concertos K 301, 302, 303, 305 and 306
6/3 20h	Avery Fisher Hall		Violin and piano Concertos K 296, 376, 377 and 378
6/12-13-14-15	Avery Fisher Hall		Symphony N°.39

FOR INFORMATION, PLEASE PHONE THE LINCOLN CENTER (212) 877 1800

* PAVILLONS CHRISTOFLE : UNITED STATES: 9515 Brighton Way BEVERLY HILLS, CA 90210 – 900 North Michigan Ave. CHICAGO, IL 60611
680 Madison Ave. NEW YORK, NY 10021 – 140 Grant Ave. SAN FRANCISCO, CA 94108
GREECE :   5 rue Koumbari Kolanaki ATHENS – 8 rue Neofitou Vamva ATHENS 138
293 Av. Kifissias KIFISSIA – 7 rue Pavlou Mela THESSALONIQUE

THE MOZART YEAR IN
GREECE

THE MOZART YEAR IN
HONG KONG

THE MOZART YEAR IN
ITALY

THE MOZART YEAR IN
JAPAN

DATE	VENUE	TELEPHONE	EVENT
SAN FRANCISCO*			
5/22 to 6/30	(415) 431 5400		Festival "Mozart and his day": (operas, ballets, plays, symphonies)
6/1-4-7-11-13-16-22	War Memorial Opera House		The Magic Flute
	(415) 864 3330		
6/2-9-15-19-21	War Memorial Opera House		The Marriage of Figaro
6/14-18-20-23-26-28	War Memorial Opera House		Così fan tutte
6/27-29 20h	Masonic Auditorium (415) 776 4917		Lucio Silla
6/30 14h	Stern Grove (415) 864 3330		La finta giardiniera
ATHENS*			
			ATHENS FESTIVAL DEVOTED TO MOZART
19/7	Odéon Hérode Atticus (1) 323 00 49**		A Mozart overture
13/8	Odéon Hérode Atticus		The Magic Flute (overture); "Prague" Symphony Nº.38
10/9	Odéon Hérode Atticus		Overture to Don Giovanni; Concerto for 2 pianos K 365,
			"Jupiter" Symphony Nº.41
11/9	Odéon Hérode Atticus		"Haffner" Symphony Nº.35; Violin Concerto;
			"Linz" Symphony Nº.36
HONG KONG*			
28/12 20h	Radio 4, RTHK		Concert by the finalists of the Asian Competition for the Mozart Bicentenary
	FOR INFORMATION, PHONE 734 9009 OR 722 6389		
FLORENCE			
June	Teatro della Pergola		54th MUSICAL MAY:
	(55) 247 96 51		The Marriage of Figaro
MILAN*			
23/4 21h15	Milan Conservatoire, Verdi Hall		Quintets K 515 and 516, Quartet
	(6) 79 53 93		
22-29/10 21h15	Milan Conservatoire, Verdi Hall		Quartet K 387
19/11 21h15	Milan Conservatoire, Verdi Hall		Quartet K 387
3/12 21h	San Marco Church		Mass in C minor, Requiem (to be confirmed)
	(2) 29 00 25 98		
ROME*			
16/4	Austrian Cultural Institute		Concilium Musicum (Quartet)
	(6) 322 47 02 or 05		
May	Austrian Cultural Institute		Duet for violin and piano
Autumn	Austrian Cultural Institute		Conference: "Why Mozart"
Autumn	Austrian Cultural Institute		String quartet
7/11	Austrian Cultural Institute		Piano concerto
24-28/11	Austrian Cultural Institute		Symposium: "Current Studies on Mozart"
OSAKA*			
April-May	(3) 35 02 1461**		Tour by the Salzburg Mozarteum Orchestra to several large cities

* PAVILLONS CHRISTOFLE : HONG KONG :   18, Ground Floor G18B the Landmark Gloucester Tower LANDMARK
103, 1st Basement Kowloon Hotel Midle Road KOWLOON
ITALY :   Corso Venezia, 6   20110 MILAN – Via Bocca di Leone, 72   00187 ROME

** TOURIST OFFICE

THE MOZART YEAR IN
SINGAPORE

THE MOZART YEAR IN
SWITZERLAND

DATE	VENUE	TELEPHONE	EVENT
TOKYO*			
May/nov.	Kanagawa Arts Association (3) 35 02 1461**		Concerts
October	Suntory Hall (3) 37 80 5400		Concerts: Mozart Festival (New York Orchestra)
Oct./nov.	Roppongi, Shibuya (3) 34 08 0111 (Wave)		Mozart exhibitions
14/11 to 15/12	Suntory Museum		Mozart Exhibition, 50 concerts (details later)
17/11	Musical Arts Centre of the Kunitachi University (3) 35 02 1461**		Idomeneo
21/11	Musashino House of Culture (3) 35 02 1461**		Idomeneo
November	Suntory Hall		International Mozart Symposium
SINGAPORE*			
Beg-April		339 6622	Kegelstatt Trio : Duets for viola and violin, Quartet for piano in G minor
GENEVA*			
28/4, 1-4-6-9-11-13-16-18/5 20h	Grand Théâtre de Genève (22) 21 23 18		Don Giovanni
Eté Summer	Cathedral		Television: broadcast of a serial on Mozart
15/12	(22) 738 52 00**		Mass in C minor
LAUSANNE*			
September	Théâtre municipal (22) 312 64 33		The Magic Flute
LUCERNE			
			SACRED MUSIC CONCERTS
16/4	18h15	Jesuit Church	Adagio and Rondo K 617
28/4	20h15	House of Fine Arts	Handel's Messiah, Mozart version
30/4		Stadtheater	The Abduction from the Seraglio
4/5	20h15	Matthäus Church	Regina coeli K 127; Litaniae Lauretanae K 109; Kyrie K 89
9/5	9h30	Franciscan Church	Mass in C major K 220
	17h	Jesuit Church	
19/5	17h	Jesuit Church	Trinitatis Mass
26/5	20h15	Cathedral	Solemn Vespers of a Confessor
30/5	17h	Jesuit Church	Kyrie K 33; Scande coeli limina; Tantum ergo; Osanna; Ave verum corpus
30/5	20h15	Jesuit Church	Litaniae de venerabili altaris sacramento; 4 short religious pieces K 47, 117, 222 and 260
30/6	17h	Jesuit Church	Missa longa K 262; Inter natos mulierium
15/8	09h30	Franciscan Church	Litaniae Lauretanae K 195
	17h	Jesuit Church	
25/8	17h	Jesuit Church	Coronation Mass
25/8	20h15	Jesuit Church	Solemn Vespers of a Confessor
15/9	17h	Jesuit Church	Misa brevis K 258
15/9	20h15	Jesuit Church	La Betulia Liberata
27/10	17h	Jesuit Church	Missa brevis K 115
1/11	15h	Jesuit Church	Mass in C major K 257

* PAVILLONS CHRISTOFLE : JAPAN :   Palais Royal B1 Royal Hotel 5-3-68 Nakanoshima Kita-Ku OSAKA
Akasaka New Otani Hotel and Tower 4-1, Kioi Cho-Chiyoda-Ku TOKYO
SINGAPORE :   Hilton Hotel 2nd Floor Orchard Road SINGAPORE

** TOURIST OFFICE

THE MOZART YEAR IN
THAILAND

DATE		VENUE	TELEPHONE	EVEN
1/11	20h15	Jesuit Church		"Dominica Vespers "
23/11	20h15	Jesuit Church		Adagio/Allegro K 594; Andante K 616; Adagio/Rondo K 617
24/11	10h	Jesuit Church		Missa brevis K 194
26/11	20h15	Jesuit Church		Misericordias Domini; Venite populi; Dixit und magnificat;
				2 church songs K 343; Sonate da Chiesa
5/12	20h15	Jesuit Church		Requiem; Maurerische Trauermusik; Ave verum corpus
6/12	17h	Academy of Sacred Music		Symposium: Mozart's Requiem (interpretation and arrangements)
7/12	20h15	Jesuit Church		Closing concert: Requiem; Kyrie K 341
8/12	9h	Franciscan Church		Missa brevis K 275; Sub tuum praesidium K 198;
				Sancta Maria mater Dei K 273
15/12	17h	Jesuit Church		Missa brevis K 192
24/12	23h	Jesuit Church		Midnight Mass: Missa brevis K 259
25/12	10h	Jesuit Church		Dominicus Mass K 66
29/12	17h	Jesuit Church		Missa brevis K 140
31/12	19h30	Jesuit Church		Te Deum laudamus

FOR INFORMATION, PLEASE PHONE THE 1991 MOZART SOCIETY (41) 22 43 18

BANGKOK*

August	Shangri-La Hotel		(2) 236 7777	Exhibition on the life of Mozart

* PAVILLONS CHRISTOFLE : SWITZERLAND: 30 rue du Rhône Place de la Fusterie 1204 GENEVA
　　　　　　　　　　　　　　　　　　10 rue de Bourg 1003 LAUSANNE
　　　　　　　　　　　THAILAND :　　The Peninsula Plaza 153 Rajadamri Road BANGKOK 10330
　　　　　　　　　　　LEBANON :　　 Centre Sabbagh BEIRUT - Centre Debs KASLIK
** TOURIST OFFICE

This program is obviously not complete. The information it contains was kindly
given by those organisations contacted prior to the printing of this publication.

Program produced exclusively for Christofle by CL,A Agency.

M	T	W	T	F	S	S
	1	2	3	4	5	6
7	8	9	10	11	12	13
14	15	16	17	18	19	20
21	22	23	24	25	26	27
28	29	30	31			

JANUARY — 1st WEEK

4 Friday

8
9
10
11
12
13
14
15
16
17
18
19
20

1783 In Vienna, Mozart completes three piano concertos (Nos. 11, 12 and 13) that he wants to have published by subscription. After the Parisian publisher Sieber had refused them, they were only printed by Artoria in March 1785.

3 Thursday

8
9
10
11
12
13
14
15
16
17
18
19
20

1780 Wolfgang gives some advice on clothes to his sister and father who were to rejoin him in Milan for the premiere of *Idomeneo*: "Each of you has only to bring one black outfit - one other everyday garment so as to spare the black outfit [...] and, if you like, one nicer costume for going to the ball".

2 Wednesday

8
9
10
11
12
13
14
15
16
17
18
19
20

1773 Leopold is pleased with the success of *Lucio Silla*, whose premiere took place the previous 26 December in Milan. However, the public has not been so enthusiastic about *Mitridate* or *Ascanio*.

1 Tuesday

8
9
10
11
12
13
14
15
16
17
18
19
20

1764 The two infant prodigies and their parents are invited to the Grand Banquet , "We arrived late", writes Leopold, "and the Swiss Guard had to make room for us".

31 Monday

8
9
10
11
12
13
14
15
16
17
18
19
20

1762 The Mozart family leaves Vienna for Salzburg. Wolfgang returns in fine attire, a present from Maria-Theresa.

8

9

10

11

12

13

14

15

16

17

18

19

20

8

9

10

11

12

13

14

15

16

17

18

19

20

1769 On his return to Salzburg, Leopold regained his job and salary, as the Prince Archbishop Sigmund von Schrattenbach is as patient as he is indulgent. But scarcely has he settled back home than he is already dreaming of a new journey, this time to Italy, to complete young Wolfgang's musical education.

1770 In Verona, the general tax inspector for Venice asks the painter Cignardi to do Mozart's portrait. In every Italian village people are grabbing hold of the infant prodigy which almost causes riots as everyone wants to see and touch him.

Portrait of Maria Leszczynska by Nattier. The Queen of France is seen to be very well disposed to little Wolfgang when the Mozarts were invited to Versailles.

New Year 1764: The Mozart family attend the Grand Banquet at Versailles. Letter from Paris from Leopold Mozart to his landlady, Maria Theresa Hagenauer, 1 February 1764.

The most extraordinary event took place at the Grand Banquet on New Year's Evening [...] Wolfgangus was honoured to be close to the Queen for the whole evening with whom he conversed and chatted, often kissing her hand and taking the food which she gave him from the table and eating next to her. The Queen speaks German like you and I. But since the King understands nothing, she translated everything our heroic Wolfgang said for him. Now, it must be said that the King never takes his meals in public, except Sunday evening when the entire royal family dines together. However, when there is an important celebration like New Year, Easter, Whitsun, etc., they call it a Grand Banquet, to which only distinguished people are admitted.

M	T	W	T	F	S	S
	1	2	3	4	5	6
7	8	9	10	11	12	13
14	15	16	17	18	19	20
21	22	23	24	25	26	27
28	29	30	31			

JANUARY   2ND WEEK

7 Monday
8
9
10
11
12
13
14
15
16
17
18
19
20

1770 Wolfgang, still in Verona, describes the picturesque street scenes during the carnival to Nannerl.

8 Tuesday
8
9
10
11
12
13
14
15
16
17
18
19
20

1779 In Munich, Wolfgang saw Aloysia who has forgotten their tender feelings and has become engaged. As a chivalrous farewell gesture, he offers the aria *Popoli di Tessaglia* that he has completed to this unfaithful lady.

9 Wednesday
8
9
10
11
12
13
14
15
16
17
18
19
20

1782 Wolfgang is still trying in vain to win over Leopold on his proposed marriage. His father replies that the mother and tutor of Constance Weber should be condemned to sweep the streets with a notice around their necks bearing the words "corrupters of youth".

10 Thursday
8
9
10
11
12
13
14
15
16
17
18
19
20

1770 Wolfgang has just arrived in Mantua. In spite of the season, his skin looks tanned. This "yellow complexion" was to displease his sister Nannerl when they met.

11 Friday
8
9
10
11
12
13
14
15
16
17
18
19
20

1787 Mozart arrives in Prague where the Count of Thun has invited him to the restaging of the *Marriage of Figaro* and where he meets his friends the Duscheks.. He will be the idol of the people of Prague during the entire visit.

12 Saturday

8

9

10

11

12

13

14

15

16

17

18

19

20

1770 Wolfgang has just attended a performance of *Demetrios* de Hasse. "The prima donna sings well, but without sufficient movement. Yet, when you do not see her perform, but only sing, you would believe that she is not singing; she does not manage to open her mouth and agonise with all the music, this is not new to us".

13 Sunday

8

9

10

11

12

13

14

15

16

17

18

19

20

1775 First performance of *La finta giardiniera* in Munich, to a thunder of applause. The premiere was initially set for 29 December, but had to be postponed, as from the first rehearsals the opera had pleased the singers so much that they demanded a little longer to learn it better.

Frontispiece from the first edition of "La finta giardiniera", a one-act comic opera, on a Calzabigi libretto, which had been commissioned from Mozart for the Munich carnival season. But the young composer had had the greatest difficulty in obtaining leave of absence from the Prince Archbishop of Salzburg, who did not even attend the triumphant premiere performance. He came however to Munich on 16 January, but greeted the compliments given him for his young musician with both an annoyed and embarrassed shaking of his head, visibly displeased to see him escape his authority.

13 January 1775, first performance of the opera "La finta giardiniera" (K 196). Letter from Munich to his mother and sister in Salzburg, 14 January 1775.

God be praised. My opera was staged yesterday, the 13th, and it was so successful that I cannot describe the applause to Mama. Firstly, the theatre was so full that many people had to return home. After each aria, there was such a frightening uproar of applause and calls of *Viva il Maestro*. Their Highnesses the Princess Elect [Maria Anna Sophie of Bavaria] and the Dowager Princess [Maria Antonia of Saxony], who were either side of me, also gave me a *bravo*; at the end of the opera, at the moment when all is silent before the ballet starts, only applause and shouts of *bravo* were heard. It had hardly stopped when someone would start again, and so on. Then I went with Papa into a room through which the Prince Elect (Maximillian II of Bavaria) and the entire court were to pass. I kissed the hands of Their Highnesses the Prince and Princess Elect as well as those of other dignitaries who have been so gracious. Very early this morning, His Grace the Prince Bishop of Chiemsee sent someone here to congratulate me because the opera had pleased everyone so much. We will not be returning straightaway, and Mama must not even wish this for she well knows how good it is to relax a little - we will be coming back quite soon.

M	T	W	T	F	S	S
	1	2	3	4	5	6
7	8	9	10	11	12	13
14	15	16	17	18	19	20
21	22	23	24	25	26	27
28	29	30	31			

JANUARY   3rd WEEK

14 Monday

8

9

10

11

12

13

14

15

16

17

18

19

20

1785 Mozart completes the sixth quartet of the series dedicated to Haydn, a series begun in 1783.

15 Tuesday

8

9

10

11

12

13

14

15

16

17

18

19

20

1779 Wolfgang returns to Salzburg, in deep depression, and is taken firmly in hand by his father. Two days later, he will be appointed court organist by decree.

16 Wednesday

8

9

10

11

12

13

14

15

16

17

18

19

20

1770 Mantua makes this "unrivalled child' the great celebrity of its philharmonic concert, by including no less than fourteen pieces which make full use of his talents for composition and interpretation.

17 Thursday

8

9

10

11

12

13

14

15

16

17

18

19

20

1778 Musical life in Mannheim has lost some of its impetus because of the departure of Charles-Theodore for Munich (where he succeeds Maximillian III). Also, Wolfgang agrees to leave the city for Kircheim, Poland, residence of the Princess of Orange.

18 Friday

8

9

10

11

12

13

14

15

16

17

18

19

20

1765 In London, Wolfgang dedicates to Queen Charlotte six sonatas for harpsichord with violin or flute accompaniment which he composed in Chelsea the previous year.

19 Saturday

8

9

10

11

12

13

14

15

16

17

18

19

20

1787 Mozart has a euphoric time in the Bohemian capital. After personally conducting *The Marriage*, he has his new *Prague* symphony performed. The triumph is unprecedented in the city's annals. Following this memorable concert, the composer improvises marvellously and at length on the piano in front of an ecstatic crowd.

20 Sunday

8

9

10

11

12

13

14

15

16

17

18

19

20

1775 After the triumph of *La finta giardiniera* in Munich, a rumour is going round that Mozart is about to enter the service of the Prince Elect of Bavaria Maximillian III. A prospect which would fulfil the wishes of Wolfgang and Leopold, but alas nothing comes of it.

This portrait of a very romantic, but not very true to life, Mozart dates from the 19th century.

On 14 January 1778, Mozart receives a visit from the Assistant Choirmaster at the Court of Mannheim, Father George Joseph Vogler (1749-1814). Letter from Mozart to his father who is in Salzburg, Mannheim, 17 January 1778.
At 11 a.m., a Supreme Court Councillor came to see me with Mr Vogler. The latter was absolutely determined to get to know me. [...]. He had brought along two pianos, tuned together, and his tiresome printed sonatas. On his express request, I had also to fetch my sonatas [K 279-284]. *N.B.* Before the meal, he had massacred my concerto [K 246] *prima vista.* He played the first movement *prestissimo,* the andante *allegro,* and the rondo truly *prestissimo.* Generally he played the bass part any other way but that written and sometimes changed the harmony as well as the melody. Moreover, at this speed, it is not possible any other way.

	M	T	W	T	F	S	S
		1	2	3	4	5	6
	7	8	9	10	11	12	13
	14	15	16	17	18	19	20
	21	22	23	24	25	26	27
	28	29	30	31			

JANUARY   4th WEEK

25 Friday

24 Thursday

23 Wednesday

22 Tuesday

21 Monday

1790 Haydn and Puchberg watch over the last rehearsals for *Cosi fan tutte*.

1783 Wolfgang and Constance give a ball in the new appartment into which they have just moved.

1782 Mozart experiences some upsets in his lovelife. In his opposition to this love for Constance, his father only serves to bring them closer together. "If I could have a written promise from God that I would not fall sick and will stay heathy, oh how I would marry my dear girl today", is what he writes.

1770 Wolfgang and his father are in Milan, with spirits high, for they have received a warm welcome from the Governor General of Lombardy, Count Firmian, who is a personal friend of the Prince Archbishop Sigmund.

1778 Aware of the Princess of Orange's love of singing, Mozart is accompanied at Kircheim Poland, by a very young woman singer who, he thinks, will make much of his compositions: Aloysia Weber, cousin of the composer Carl Maria von Weber.

26 Saturday

8

9

10

11

12

13

14

15

16

17

18

19

20

1790 Premiere in Milan of *Cosi fan tutte*. The success is justified and it may even be said that it is the first time that such unanimity is reached on a Mozart opera.

27 Sunday

8

9

10

11

12

13

14

15

16

17

18

19

20

1756 Birth in Salzburg of the seventh child of Leopold Mozart and Anna Maria Perti, a boy called Johann Chrysostomus Wolfgang Theophilus (i.e. "beloved of the gods") hence the equivalent in Latin, Amadeus.

Wolfgang Amadeus Mozart at the age of eight or nine years, by Johann Zoffany. The authenticity of this portrait painted in England has been questioned.

27 January 1756: birth of Wolfgang Amadeus Mozart (he will be christened the day after). Letter from Salzburg from Leopold Mozart to his publishers in Augsburg, Johann Jakob Lotter. Salzburg, 9 February 1756.

Moreover, I wish to announce that on 27 January, at 8 p.m., my wife happily gave birth to a son. But they had to take away the placenta from her. Then she became incredibly weakened. Today (Thanks be to God), mother and child are well. She send you both her kind regards. Our son is called Joannes Chrisostomus, Wolfgang., Gottlieb.

In 1761, young Wolfgang makes rapid progress on the keyboard. A progress that Leopold notes in Nannerl's "Book of the Harpsichord" (1759).

24 January: Wolfgangerl has learned this piece, three days before his fifth birthday, at half past nine. 26 January: Wolfgangerl in half an hour has learned this minuet and trio, the day before his fifth birthday, at half past nine.

M	T	W	T	F	S	S
	1	2	3	4	5	6
7	8	9	10	11	12	13
14	15	16	17	18	19	20
21	22	23	24	25	26	27
28	29	30	31			

JANUARY　　5ᵗʰ WEEK　　　　　　　　　　　FEBRUARY

1 Friday
8

31 Thursday
8

30 Wednesday
8

29 Tuesday
8

28 Monday
8

9 · 9 · 9 · 9 · 9

10 · 10 · 10 · 10 · 10

11 · 11 · 11 · 11 · 11

12 · 12 · 12 · 12 · 12

13 · 13 · 13 · 13 · 13

14 · 14 · 14 · 14 · 14

15 · 15 · 15 · 15 · 15

16 · 16 · 16 · 16 · 16

17 · 17 · 17 · 17 · 17

18 · 18 · 18 · 18 · 18

19 · 19 · 19 · 19 · 19

20 · 20 · 20 · 20 · 20

1764 Leopold, who has always cultivated a streak of puritanism, writes: "Are the women in Paris so pretty? In truth, I would not say so as they are as false and painted as the Berchtesgaden dolls."

1778 Mozart sends some verse in his own style to his mother, who is soon to accompany him to Paris:
"We travel the world
"But we have hardly any money
"Nonetheless we are in high spirits
"And nobody is congested
"I am with people
"Who have a turd in their belly
"But who let it drop
"Before as well as after the feasting."

1768 The infant prodigy, who amazed the Viennese at six years, of age, no longer surprises them at eleven. To stimulate public interest, Leopold thinks of confronting his son with the greatest composers of the day. Wolfgang is hard at work on the score for *La finta semplice*, but the opera will be refused in Vienna.

1781 The Premiere in Munich of *Idomeneo*. The work is well received but will not however run very long. It is true that the critics expressed some reservations.

1777 Mozart dedicates a piano concerto to Mlle Jeunehomme, a Parisian virtuoso.

		3 Sunday
		8
2 Saturday		
8		9
9		10
10		11
11		12
12		13
13		14
14		15
15		16
16		17
17		18
18		19
19		20
20		

1778 Returning euphorically from Kircheim Poland. Wolfgang has fallen in love with Aloysia Weber. The reaction of his father whom he immediately informed of his feelings of admiration was not slow in coming. Leopold is already proclaiming this an unsuitable alliance and orders his son to leave for Paris.

1786 Mozart finishes a singspiel, *Der Schauspiele Direktor*, which has been commissioned from him by Joseph II and which must be played during the visit of the Governor of the Low Countries. The piece will be sung on 7 February in Schonbrunn on the same programme as a Salieri opera, *Prima la musica, poi la parole.*.

Score of "Idomeneo ", an opera commissioned by Charles-Theodore of Bavaria.

29 January 1781: First pperformance in Munich of "Idomeneo" (K 366) at the Court Theatre. Mozart from Munich to his father in Salzburg, 27 December 1780. The prince Elect [Charles-Theodore] shouted *Bravo!* very loudly. And when I came to kiss his hand, he said: "This opera will be delightful; It will surely bring you honour." Not knowing whether he would be able to stay long enough, we had to play the aria concertante and the storm from the second act. He then expressed his approval to me in a very friendly way and said laughing: "You would not imagine that such great things are hidden inside such a little head." *Munich, 30 december 1780.*

Forgive me for writing so little this time - for I am up to the ears in work. The third act is not quite finished, and as there is no separate ballet but only a *divertimento* incorporated into the opera, I will be equally honoured to compose the music for it [K 367].

Vienna
The little prince

The imperial capital was a happy city. Under the reign of Maria Theresa and Joseph II, the combination of absolutism and simplicity gave the Austrian monarchy the nature of a family authority. The child Mozart so quickly felt at ease with himself that he jumped on the lap of the Empress and bestowed her with kisses. At least that is how Leopold Mozart tells it, as the indulgent chronicler of his child's exploits and of the favours shown by princes.

In the city, the relatively easy life and peaceful good humour encouraged the blossoming of extremely diverse individual talents. Immigrants were immediately integrated. And as music reigned supreme in this blessed city, a prodigious child musician was sure to receive a good welcome. Thus it is Vienna where Mozart begins his professional life at the age of six: concerts, receptions, composition, success, fatigue...always avoiding with unselfconscious grace that change in refinement and sensitivity which usually affects infant prodigies. His father was a self-made impressario, secretary, treasurer, in the style of a bear tamer. Wolfgang remains a natural, not at all intimidated by the majesty of power nor by the glare of notoriety, just delighted and amused to find the world at his feet, which made so great an impression on his father. The first stay in Vienna, an extraordinary beginning to the career of a six-year-old child, from its outset reveals his deep-rooted qualities: spontaneity, assurance, intelligence, sensitivity .... When the Archduchess Marie-Antoinette (aged seven) helps

Above, Wolfgang at six years of age, wearing the superb costume in lilac watered silk given to him by Empress Maria Theresa. This portrait was not however painted at the Viennese court, but in Salzburg, where the Mozart family had settled back home in January 1763. Another picture showing Nannerl was made to hang by this one.

Left, a portrait of Joseph II, who came to the Austrian Throne in 1780 (but he had succeeded his father as Emperor in 1765). He undertook the "Germanisation" of Austria, imposing the German language in all the Hapsburg States. And as he was a fervent musician, it was natural that he should uphold the ideal of a national German opera.

Right, a picture of the good life in Vienna: the Augarten Gardens at the end of the 18th century.

him to get up after a fall on the slippery parquet, he thanks her with a kiss and promised to marry her. Nor does he disguise his feelings when he listens to a young archduke violinist: "He is playing out of tune ! It's terrible !" Nowadays, as a reaction against the image of the small inspired prodigy, we are determined to make Mozart's apprenticeship and the evolution of his character seem commonplace all the better to enable the angelic spirit of a genius to transcend ! He was a charming child whom the cosmopolitan and educated aristocracy could not resist. But he was also a child genius, as shown for example by the sublime andante of his first symphony K 16, composed at the age of eight. The seriousness of the mood, the nobility of originality, the subtlety of the instrumentation are overwhelming and exceed the imagination of Leopold. Some years later - Wolfgang would soon be twelve years old -, a second stay in Vienna will only bring disappointments. The Mozart children catch smallpox. The Archduchess Maria Josepha, fiancee to the King of Naples, dies with it ... And poor Leop old was counting upon the royal wedding to provide more opportunities to show off his children !

They are however received by Maria-Teresa and Joseph II. The atmosphere is gloomy. The Empress withdraws more and more from the public, drama, music. As for the Emperor, his taste for simplicity becomes an obsession and his concern for economy avarice. The nobility reduces its expenses in line with the imperial trend: patronage of the arts is no longer in vogue. The Emperor suggests that the young boy compose an opera and conduct it himself at the harpsichord. The local musicians are scandalised ! Any pretext is given to delay the performance of the work, this *Finta semplice* which in the end will not have first performance in Vienna, but in Salzburg the following year. "All the devils in music are unleashed to prevent a child's talent from being noticed", writes Leopold. Five years later when he returned to Vienna, Mozart seemed to have forgotten this first disappointment of his career. Vienna was saving others for him. But it was to have given him a zest for freedom, the comfort of friendship and the secret recognition of the rights of genius.

ROLAND DE CANDE

	M	T	W	T	F	S	S
					1	2	3
	4	5	6	7	8	9	10
	11	12	13	14	15	16	17
	18	19	20	21	22	23	24
	25	26	27	28			

FEBRUARY — 6th **WEEK**

4 Monday

8
9
10
11
12
13
14
15
16
17
18
19
20

1778 Finished with German opera, Wolfgang swears that only Italy can make a prima donna of Aloysia.

5 Tuesday

8
9
10
11
12
13
14
15
16
17
18
19
20

1778 Wolfgang's love for Aloysia is the despair of Leopold: "I was particularly avoiding any familiarity with people of our profession [...]. I was seeking friendship from only a higher class of persons."

6 Wednesday

8
9
10
11
12
13
14
15
16
17
18
19
20

1787 Mozart writes six German dances in Prague. Never will the "little man" have known such happiness. A few days later, he is to return to Vienna with the commission for a new opera in his pocket. This will be *Don Giovanni*.

7 Thursday

8
9
10
11
12
13
14
15
16
17
18
19
20

1770 In Milan, Wolfgang becomes acquainted with Gianbattista Sammartini. On the same day, Count Firmian gives him nine volumes on the work of Metastasio.

8 Friday

8
9
10
11
12
13
14
15
16
17
18
19
20

1784 Constance is pregnant again. Mozart abandons the composition of *the Goose of Cairo*. To put some order into his life, he notes down in a book the completion date of each of his works as well as their first two bars.

8

9

9

10

10

11

11

12

12

13

13

14

14

15

15

16

16

17

17

18

18

19

19

20

20

1770 In Milan, Wolfgang Italianises his name in a letter to his kinfolk and for the first time signs Wolfgang Amadeo.

1771 Leopold and Wolfgang make Venice their final stop on the way back from this long and fertile journey to Italy.

A Mozart medallion by Scharff.

7 February 1786, first performance in Vienna of the "Theatre Director" (K 486). The newspaper "Wiener Zeitung" of 8 February gives full details of the festivities. On Tuesday, His Majesty the Emperor [Joseph II] organised festivities in Schonbrunn in honour of the venerable governors general of the Low Countries of the Empire and a group of nobles from our city. Forty gentlemen were also invited, as well as Prince [Stanislaus] Poniatowski. All chose the lady who was to accompany them and met at 3 o'clock, in twos, in open carriages and coaches, from the Hofburg to Schonbrunn, where they went down to the Orangery. His Imperial Majesty was accompanied by the Archduchess [Maria] Christina. The Orangery had been sumptuously and finely decorated for the reception of the lunch guests. The table, set up under the orange trees, was decorated with flowers and fruits from our own country as well as abroad. Whilst His Majesty, the foreign noblemen and guests partook of their meal, wind instrument music was played by musicians from the Imperial and Royal Chamber. They left the table to attend the play performed on the stage mounted at the end of the Orangery. The play, including a piece with airs composed specially for this event and called *The Theatre Director*, was performed by actors from the German National Theatre. At the end of the play, on the Italian stage mounted at the other end of the Orangery, a *comic opera,* also composed specially for the occasion and bearing the title: *Prima la musica e poi le parole,* was performed by singers from the Court Opera.

M	T	W	T	F	S	S
			1	2	3
4	5	6	7	8	9	10
11	12	13	14	15	16	17
18	19	20	21	22	23	24
25	26	27	28

FEBRUARY   7th WEEK

11 Monday

8

9

10

11

12

13

14

15

16

17

18

19

20

1785 Mozart is present at Haydn's enthronement at the True Concord masonic lodge.

12 Tuesday

8

9

10

11

12

13

14

15

16

17

18

19

20

1778 Italy always fires Wolfgang's imagination, but his father's letter is like a cold shower. Leopold advises him to take care of a family more impoverished than the Webers: his own.

13 Wednesday

8

9

10

11

12

13

14

15

16

17

18

19

20

1782 "Whatever the weather, from 6 a.m. my hair is ready and at 7 a.m. I am completely dressed. Then I write until 9 o'clock. From 9 a.m. to 1 p.m. I have my lessons - then I dine.. Before 5 p.m. impossible to work. [...] Otherwise, I write until 9 o'clock. Then I go to my dear Constance's, and between 10.30 and 11 o'clock I return home."

14 Thursday

8

9

10

11

12

13

14

15

16

17

18

19

20

1785 Leopold visits his son in Vienna. Wolfgang's success incites mixed feelings in him, with a mingling of pride, suspicion and jealousy. Haydn, after hearing the last three of the quartets dedicated to him, declares that in his opinion Mozart is the greater.

15 Friday

8

9

10

11

12

13

14

15

16

17

18

19

20

1778 The flautist Wendling and the oboist Ramm take the road to Paris, abandoning their friend Wolfgang, whose passion for Aloysia still keeps him in Mannheim.

16 Saturday

8
9
10
11
12
13
14
15
16
17
18
19
20

1778 Leopold's letter to Wolfgang: "My son! you are too high-spirited and too hasty! Your character has completely changed since childhood. As a child and adolescent, you were more serious than puerile and when you were at the piano or occupied with music; nobody dared make the slightest joke."

17 Sunday

8
9
10
11
12
13
14
15
16
17
18
19
20

1770 Leopold writes to his wife from Milan: "Wolfgang will not come to any harm because of the food or drink... Often he eats little during the day, but he is stout and healthy".

11 February 1785, Leopold Mozart visits his son in Vienna and attends his first concert the same evening. He writes to his daughter on 16 February.

Your brother has a pretty appartment with all sorts of amenities included in the house, as you would expect when you know he pays a rent of 460 florins. This very Friday we went at 6 o'clock to his first subscribed Concert, where were gathered a crowd of people of quality. Each pays a gold sovereign or three ducats for the six Lenten Concerts. They take place at the Mehlgrube, and the room only costs him half a gold sovereign per evening [...] On Saturday evening, Mr. Joseph Haydn and the two Barons Tinti came to see us; they interpreted the new quartets, but only the three new ones (K 458-464-465) that he has composed [...] Mr. Haydn told me: "I vow before God, as an honest man, your son is the greatest composer I know, personally or by reputation; he has refinement and, moreover, the greatest knowledge of composition."

Leopold who knew how to exploit the achievements of the infant prodigy Wolfang.

M	T	W	T	F	S	S
			1	2	3
4	5	6	7	8	9	10
11	12	13	14	15	16	17
18	19	20	21	22	23	24
25	26	27	28

FEBRUARY — 8th WEEK

18 Monday
8
9
10
11
12
13
14
15
16
17
18
19
20

1770 Concert in Milan at Count Firmian's. Masked ball at the opera in the evening.

19 Tuesday
8
9
10
11
12
13
14
15
16
17
18
19
20

1778 Leopold's epistle has its effect. Wolfgang admits that Aloysia is perhaps too young to chance her luck in Italy.

20 Wednesday
8
9
10
11
12
13
14
15
16
17
18
19
20

1790 Death of Joseph II. As a mark of mourning, the theatres will remain closed until 12 April. The performances of *Cosi fan tutte* are interrupted.

21 Thursday
8
9
10
11
12
13
14
15
16
17
18
19
20

1765 Leopold in London organises a concert where Wolfgang's first symphonies will be performed. But the receipts are meager; and Mozart's purse is emptying at a more than distrubing rapidity.

22 Friday
8
9
10
11
12
13
14
15
16
17
18
19
20

1778 Wolfgang takes up his pen again to plead his case. Will he succeed in making his father understand how sincere is his love for Aloysia.

23 Saturday

8

9

10

11

12

13

14

15

16

17

18

19

20

1767 In Salzburg, Wolfgang learns much in the company of Michel Haydn with whom he is going to write the oratorio *The Obligation of the First Commandment*, commissioned by the Archbishop Sigmud. The work will be performed in March.

24 Sunday

8

9

10

11

12

13

14

15

16

17

18

19

20

1790 Mozart composes his *Concerto n° 26 for piano in D Major* known as the Coronation, as it be performed on 15 October in Frankfurt during the festivities organised for the coronation of Leopold II.

A view of Vienna at the time of Wolfgang's debut there, by Bernardo Bellotto.

During this week in 1785, Mozart and his father set a good pace for Vienna, Leopold writes to his daughter on 21 February.

Friday 18th, we ate at young Stephanie's where there were only four; Mr. Lebrun , his wife, Karl Cannabich and a priest. In short, it must be said first of all that it is not possible to think of fasting here. Only meat dishes were served and the pheasant was served with cabbage; the remainder was princely; at the end, oysters, the finest confectionery, not forgetting the many bottles of Champagne. And always coffee, that goes without saying. From there we went to your brother's second concert, at 7 o'clock, at the Mehlgrube. Once again it was splendid. Henry played a concerto for violin. Mr. Stephanie immediately inquired after you and we did not stop speaking of old memories. Here we have never ever eaten leanly. Yesterday, 20th, we had a meal for 21 at Mr. Muller's the actor. It was also remarkable but not as exaggerated. He is obliged to take a large appartment as he has eight children, and he pays 700 florins per year. Mr. Stephanie has quite a small appartment, - but he pays 500 florins because it is located in the Michaelerplatz, close to the theatre. Wednesday 23rd and Monday 28th, there are two concerts by Mr. Lebrun and his wife in the theatre. All the boxes for the first concert have been taken since the 18th. These people are going to receive enormous sums of money.

M	T	W	T	F	S	S
				1	2	3
4	5	6	7	8	9	10
11	12	13	14	15	16	17
18	19	20	21	22	23	24
25	26	27	28			

FEBRUARY   9th WEEK

MARCH

1 Friday
8

28 Thursday
8

27 Wednesday
8

26 Tuesday
8

25 Monday
8

9

10

11

12

13

14

15

16

17

18

19

20

1778 Leopold to his son, still in Mannheim: "You only listen to praise and flattery."

1778 As for Wolfgang, he exorcises the pain of his next separation by producing more arias for Aloysia.

1773 Leopold, who had requested a position at the Tuscan Court for Wolfgang, recieves a negative response from the Grand Duke. Now there is nothing to detain them any longer in Italy and they hurry to Salsburg.

1791 Vienna. *The Triumph of the Ladies,* a quadrille for orchestra.

1766 The Mozart family is in The Hague. For the festivities accompanying the enthronement of William V, Wolfgang composes a Quolibet Galimatias Musicum, a sort of musical medley with a comic effect.

2 Saturday

8 ....

9 ....

10 ....

11 ....

12 ....

13 ....

14 ....

15 ....

16 ....

17 ....

18 ....

19 ....

20

1786 In Vienna, Wolfgang works on the score for *The Marriage* in the spacious and comfortable residence on the Schullerstrasse, since called the "Figarihaus". In this auspicious period, he also writes his *Piano Concerto Nº 23 in A Major.*

3 Sunday

8 ....

9 ....

10 ....

11 ....

12 ....

13 ....

14 ....

15 ....

16 ....

17 ....

18 ....

19 ....

20

1783 Vienna. *Music for a carnival pantomine* written for a string quarter (K 446). Wolfgang basks in great joy: he has a pleasant house, a loving and easy-to-live-with wife and generous friends. He will soon have even a horse to ride.

Salzburg, 28 February 1763: first public appearance of Wolf gang on the occasion of the birthday of the Prince Archbishop Sigmund von Schrattenbach. Extract from the "Court Diary", 28 February 1763.

After the ceremony, the following entertainment took place: [...] Mr Lolli, Assistant Choirmaster and Mr Mozart, *musicus*, Assistant Choirmaster [...] At 5 o'clock, the whole court was resplendent in gala dress in the audience room where His Grace the Prince received the respectful wishes of everyone, and at 6 o'clock, after the Ave Maria, he went with his subjects into the council chamber where they attended not the usual reception but a vocal music concert given by several virtuosos amongst whom also appeared the small 7-year-old son (Wolfgang) of the new Assistant Choirmaster and his 10-year-old daughter [Nannerl], who were heard on the instrument [keyboard], the son also played everything on the violin that was asked of him, which concluded this fine birthday celebration.

Sigmund von Strattenbach, Prince Archbishop of Salzburg, who had a not very hard-working Assistant Choirmaster in the person of Leopold Mozart.

SIGISMUND⁹ CHRISTOPHOR⁹
Archiepiſc. et S.R.I. Princeps Salis =
burgenſis, S. Sedis Apoſtolicæ Legatus
Natus, Germaniæ Primas, ex Illuſtriſsi

Towards Christmas time 1763 (some months before the death of Rameau) a Viennese gentleman attended the services at the Royal Chapel at Versailles in company with his small son. He was to write to his wife remaining in Vienna: "Here I have heard good and bad music. All that for the voice alone was meaningless, cold as ice, miserable, French

in a nutshell." A judgement a trifle severe... Happily, what follows is more favourable: "The choirs are all very good, excellent even, and for this reason I went every day with my little man to the King's Mass to hear the choirs who always sing the *Motets.*"
This Viennese gentleman's name was Leopold Mozart and his "little man" Wolfgang Gottlieb, called Amadeus. Arriving in Paris on 19 November, both were to stay at the Hotel de Beau vais with the Count Van Eyck, Ambassador of Bavaria. There they had found a small colony

of German or Austrian musicians: Eckart, Schobert especially, and the famous Grimm who opened the doors of all the salons to them. At the beginning of December, they had paid a first visit to Versailles and saw, if not the Royal Family, at least Mme de Pompadour, "a really beautiful person," as Leopold writes. On 1 January 1764, Leopold and Wolfgang are invited to the King's Grand Couvert: "Wolfgang stood at the side of the Queen to talk incessantly to her, amuse her, kiss her hands and eat all the tasty morsels that she benevolently passed to him. The Queen speaks German as well as us, but the king understands not one iota". And the music ? Mozart plays; famous painting have preserved all that for us. He hears: the Versailles choirs, but also the music of Schobert which will leave some impression on him. "Truthfully, I can say that every day God works new wonders through this child. Before we return home (God willing), he will already be capable of taking up service at Court. He accompanies taking the bass part at public concerts..." But above all Wolfgang

composes: six sonatas for harpsichord with violin accompaniment which will be engraved in Paris and form his Opus 1: "In two weeks at the latest, we will return to Versailles, where the Duke of Anjou has arranged an audience to present Madame Victoire, the second daughter of the King and to whom is dedicated the first work, with the engraved Sonatas by the great Wolfgang." (22 February). Opus 2 (another six sonatas) will be dedicated to Mme de Tesse, Lady-in-waiting to the Dauphine.
The Mozarts left Paris on 10 April, after a second stay at Versailles. Did Wolfgang see *Bastien and Bastienne* by Favart there, the libretto for he will use in 1768 ? After his entry into the world of the sonata, another link from Versailles would be in opera. Such was the first Mozart sojourn in Paris - apparently the only time he visited Versailles. The second journey is, in effect, somewhat mysterious. Louis XV died in 1778 and the Queen of France was an Austrian who knew Mozart as a child at Schönbrunn.
("You are nice, when I get

Left, the Marchioness de Pompadour, by Quentin de la Tour. Baron Grimm introduced Wolfgang to the spiritual marchioness, friend of philosophers, who was to die of pneumonia shortly afterwards.

SONATES
POUR LE CLAVECIN
Qui peuvent se jouer avec l'Accompagnement de Violon
DEDIÉES
A MADAME VICTOIRE
DE FRANCE
Par J. G. Wolfgang Mozart de Salzbourg
Âgé de Sept ans
OEUVRE PREMIERE.
Prix 4 ℔ 4 ₰
Gravées par Mme Vendôme Ci-devant rue St. Jacques
à present rue St Honoré Vis à vis le Palais Royal.
A PARIS
aux adresses ordinaires
AVEC PRIVILEGE DU ROI.
imprimé par petit blé

Above, frontispiece of the book of sonatas for harpsichord and violin composed by Wolfgang during this first visit to France. These pieces were edited as two collections, the first dedicated to Madame Victoire, daughter of Louis XV, the second to the Countess de Tessé, mistress of the Prince de Conti whose salon was one of the most popular in the capital. Left, the gardens of the Grand Trianon at Versailles.

bigger I will marry you": she was seven years old and he five...). She is a musician, protects and helps the composers of her own country and made Gluck successful. During Mozart's stay in Paris, he was even offered the post of organist to the Royal Chapel, but it does not seem that he was interested enough to even go to Versailles - to the point that Leopold, remaining in Vienna, gets angry about it

in his letters.
He does not even make use of the letters of introduction he has, one was from Diderot; he has the opportunity to meet Beaumarchais and does not do so. What is happening ? Evidently Wolfgang is no longer the infant prodigy. Awkward and timid, is he so ill at ease in the world ? Must we believe what his friend Raaf tells us: "Mozart is not complete here. To admire Paris, he would not have had to leave half of himself in the place where I come from." Half of himself, that is Aloysia Weber, in Mannheim.
He was to leave Paris after six drab months, amongst the most empty of his existence, without having recaptured any of his former success - if it were not for one thing, very great, but without a future, the *Sinfonia concertante...*
And it is later, much later, that France will be in his mind as in *the Marriage of Figaro.*

PHILIPPE BEAUSSANT

M	T	W	T	F	S	S
			1	2	3	
4	5	6	7	8	9	10
11	12	13	14	15	16	17
18	19	20	21	22	23	24
25	26	27	28	29	30	31

MARCH   10th WEEK

4 Monday

8

9

10

11

12

13

14

15

16

17

18

19

20

1783 Yielding to the intrigues of Salieri, Joseph II dissolves the German Opera.

5 Tuesday

8

9

10

11

12

13

14

15

16

17

18

19

20

1771 In Venice, Wolfgang gives a grand concert which will be applauded by all the nobility. Leopold is very impressed by the splendour of the Doges' city.

6 Wednesday

8

9

10

11

12

13

14

15

16

17

18

19

20

1775 The Mozarts leave Munich after a very busy carnival season during which Wolfgang at the harpsichord is compared with Captain von Becke.

7 Thursday

8

9

10

11

12

13

14

15

16

17

18

19

20

1791 Vienna. Schikaneder, Director of the Auf der Wieden Theatre, comes to find Mozart at eight in the morning and drags him out of bed to commission the writing of an opera: this will be *The Magic Flute.*

8 Friday

8

9

10

11

12

13

14

15

16

17

18

19

20

1781 Munich. Mozart dedicates the scene *Misera, dove son... Ah, non so io,* of his opera Idomeneo, to the Countess Baumgarten, the acknowledged mistress of Charles-Theodore, for the favours shown to him at court.

8

9

10

11

12

13

14

15

16

17

18

19

20

1786 Mozart finally succeeds in realising an old dream : reviving *Idomeneo*. He rewrites several arias for this revival which takes place in the Viennese palace of the Prince Aucroperg.

1783 Mozart completes the *Concerto in C* K.467. His reputation as a pianist as well as a composer is at its peak.

Mozart at the harpsichord in the drawing room of the Prince de Conti, at the Temple (picture by Ollivier).

10 March 1764, first concert of the Mozart children in Paris, in the rooms of Mr Felix, St-Honore Street and Entrance. "The Avant-Coureur" of 5 March 1764 gives an account of the event, no doubt penned by Grimm.

Mr Mozart, Director of Music of H.H. the Prince Archbishop of Salzburg, has been in this capital for several months with two children of the most congenial appearance. His eleven year old daughter plays the harpsichord with distinction; you could not expect to have a more precise and brilliant performance. His son, who this month had his seventh birthday, is a real prodigy. He has all the talent and knowledge of a choirmaster. Not only does he give a surprising performance of concertos by the most famous European masters; but he himself composes. He plays from memory for hours on end, and, surrendering himself to his inspired genius, marries the most priceless themes to his immense knowledge of harmony. All those who know music are utterly surprised to see a child perform that which would have been admired in the most accomplished choirmaster. You can put this amazing child through all the tests. If you give him a piece with no bass and demand that he write the bass for it, he will do it without needing the harpsichord nor the violin, which few composers can do [...]. He will accompany by ear the tunes that are sung to him, and he will immediately improvise in an infinite number of ways. He has such great ability on the keyboard that you may spread a napkin over it without it preventing his playing with the same precision and speed.

M	T	W	T	F	S	S
				1	2	3
4	5	6	7	8	9	10
11	12	13	14	15	16	17
18	19	20	21	22	23	24
25	26	27	28	29	30	31

MARCH | 11th WEEK

11 Monday
8
9
10
11
12
13
14
15
16
17
18
19
20

1783 Mozart successfully participates in the concert organised by Aloysia. Gluck sings his praises.

12 Tuesday
8
9
10
11
12
13
14
15
16
17
18
19
20

1767 Leopold thinks about leaving Salzburg. Wolfgang is compared with the Court organist Adlgasser.

13 Wednesday
8
9
10
11
12
13
14
15
16
17
18
19
20

1778 After half an evening with the Webers, Mozart leaves Man nheim and takes the road to Paris. His mother goes with him, supplied with precise instructions on the part of Leopold.

14 Thursday
8
9
10
11
12
13
14
15
16
17
18
19
20

1772 The death of the Prince Archbishop Sigmund von Strattenbach has left the episcopal throne empty. A successor must be elected. The ballot is long. Finally, after much hesitation, the Salzburg Chapter elects Colloredo.

15 Friday
8
9
10
11
12
13
14
15
16
17
18
19
20

1770 Leaving Milan, where the Count Firmian has made a present of a gold snuffbox to his son, Leopold took the road to Parma. Wolfgang completes his first string quartet in Lodi.

16 Saturday

8

9

10

11

12

13

14

15

16

17

18

19

20

1781 Coming to Munich for the first performance of *Idomeneo*, Mozart lingers after the carnival. Colloredo directs him to rejoin him in Vienna where he has come to present his respects to the new sovereign Joseph II. Wolfgang regretfully obeys, after writing the *Gran Partita* for his friends the musicians of the Munich Orchestra.

17 Sunday

8

9

10

11

12

13

14

15

16

17

18

19

20

1781 In Vienna, in the House of the Teutonic Knights which is the residence of Colloredo, Wolfgang bitterly sees himself relegated to the level of servant: "We sit down at table at 12 o'clock - there we eat, the two body and soul valets, Mr. Controller and Mr. Pastrycook, two cooks... and my humble self; the two menservants are at the head of the table - I am honoured however to be seated before the cooks."

Aloysia Weber and her husband, Joseph Lange. Mozart to the great fury of Leopold was in love with her, but thereafter married her young sister Constance, this was not any the more pleasing to his father, who despised the Webers.

---

17 March 1781, Mozart participates in a concert at Prince Dimitri Mikhailovitch Galitzine's. On the following 24 March, he gives an account to his father.
Recently, when we have had to go to Prince Galitzine's, Brunetti [violinist to the Salzburg Court] tells me, in his usual friendly way - *tu bisogna che sei qui sta sera alle sette, per andare insieme del Prencipe Gallizin. Langerbauer* [manservant to the Prince Archbishop] *ci condurra.* Ho risposto - *Va bene, ma, se in caso mai no fossi qua alle sette in punto, ci andate pure; non serve aspettarmi - so ben dove sta, e ci verro sicuro* ["Well now, you have to be here tonight at seven o'clock so that we can go together to Prince Galitzine's. Angerbauer will take us there. I replied: All right, but if by chance I am not there at seven o'clock, go on; don't wait - I very well know where he lives, I will certainly be there." I took care to go alone for I was ashamed to go anywhere in their company. On my arrival, Mr Angerbauer was already there telling the servant to introduce me - but without paying any attention to Mr Manservant nor Mr Servant, I crossed the appartment whose doors were all open, as far as the music room. I went directly to the Prince, paid him my compliments - and stayed there talking to him at length.
On 11 March 1783, Mozart plays in his sister-in-law Aloysia Lange's concert.

M	T	W	T	F	S	S
				1	2	3
4	5	6	7	8	9	10
11	12	13	14	15	16	17
18	19	20	21	22	23	24
25	26	27	28	29	30	31

MARCH 12th WEEK

18 Monday
8
9
10
11
12
13
14
15
16
17
18
19
20

1787 Mozart revives the aria *Non so d'ondo viene* for the bass voice of Fischer.

19 Tuesday
8
9
10
11
12
13
14
15
16
17
18
19
20

1770 Leopold and Wolfgang arrive in Parma where they will make a brief stop before leaving for Bologna.

20 Wednesday
8
9
10
11
12
13
14
15
16
17
18
19
20

1784 Wolfgang in Vienna: "My first concert on the 17th of this month is fortunately over. The room was full to bursting and the new concerto I played was extraordinarily successful [no doubt the Concerto in E. Flat]. Everywhere we go it is receiving praise."

21 Thursday
8
9
10
11
12
13
14
15
16
17
18
19
20

1785 Despite his wishes for a German opera, Mozart will repudiate what Klein had sent him from Mannheim, *Rudolf von Hapsburg*, and he will arrange *the Marriage of Figaro* as a comic opera, with the complicity of Da Ponte.

22 Friday
8
9
10
11
12
13
14
15
16
17
18
19
20

1784 Vienna. *Piano Concerto N°. 16 in C Major*, together with N°. 15, concertos which "leave him sweating."

23 Saturday	**24** Sunday
8	8
9	9
10	10
11	11
12	12
13	13
14	14
15	15
16	16
17	17
18	18
19	19
20	20

1778 Wolfgang put his foot on Parisian soil at the end of a journey made sad and tiresome since he was nostalgic for Mannheim. But here he is consoled to find two of his good friends from over there who preceeded him: Ramm and Wendling.

1770 Leopold and Wolfgang arrive in Bologna where they are honoured to be introduced to Father Martini, the highest musical authority in all Italy, who, fascinated by the extraordinary gifts of the young boy, will receive him at home on several occasions and lavish friendship and advice on him.

Portrait of Joseph II. Like all the children of Maria-Theresa, the Emperor greatly appreciated music and personally played several instruments.

24 March 1783, Mozart gives a concert at the Theatre of the Viennese Court in the presence of Joseph II. Letter of 29 March to his father.

The Emperor was also present [...] - He usually sends money to the cash-office before his arrival at the theatre, if not I might have expected more for his satisfaction was limitless -he sent 25 ducats. The pieces were as follows: 1) the new *Haffner Symphony* [K 385]; 2) Mme Lange sang the aria with four instruments from my Munich opera [this is *Idomeneo*, K 366], *Se il padre perdei*; 3) I played the third of my subscribed concertos [K 415]; 4) Adamberger sang the Paugmarten scene [K 369]; 5) the small *sinfonia concertante* from my latest *Final Music* [K 320]; 6) I played the Concerto in D Major [K 175]; 7) Mlle Teyber sang the scene from my last Milan opera [*Lucio Silla*, K 135], *Parto, m'affretto*; 8) I played a short fugue alone (because the Emperor was there).

M	T	W	T	F	S	S
				1	2	3
4	5	6	7	8	9	10
11	12	13	14	15	16	17
18	19	20	21	22	23	24
25	26	27	28	29	30	31

MARCH 13th WEEK

25 Monday

8
9
10
11
12
13
14
15
16
17
18
19
20

1778 Wolfgang meets Grimm again in Paris, who introduces him to Jean Le Gros, Director of the Spiritual Concerts.

26 Tueday

8
9
10
11
12
13
14
15
16
17
18
19
20

1785 Vienna. *Geselllenreise* ("The Voyage of the Companions") the first work Mozart composed for a masonic meeting.

27 Wednesday

8
9
10
11
12
13
14
15
16
17
18
19
20

1770 Bologna "What gives me special pleasure is that here we are well liked. And Wolfgang especially is appreciated here even more than in other Italian cities, because here live a large number of masters and scholars", writes Leopold.

28 Thursday

8
9
10
11
12
13
14
15
16
17
18
19
20

1771 Leopold and Wolfgang return to Salzburg where Anna Maria and Nannerl have been waiting for them for fifteen months.

29 Friday

8
9
10
11
12
13
14
15
16
17
18
19
20

1783 In Vienna, the Emperor by his presence condescends to raise the tone of the concert organised by Mozart. About ten pieces on the programme, including two symphonies and two concertos.

	31 Sunday
	8
30 Saturday	9
8	
9	10
10	11
11	12
12	13
13	14
14	15
15	16
16	17
17	18
18	19
19	20
20	

1784 Vienna, *Quintet for piano and strings in E Flat,* K 452. This is the period when Mozart works with Haydn. In the shadows, his enemies, disturbed by the adulation, are plotting intrigues to discredit him.

1768 The prolonged absences of his Assistant Choirmaster causes the indulgent Sigmund to decide purely and simply to suspend his salary for as long as he is not performing his duties.

26 March 1770, first meeting in Bologna between Father Martini, the ultimate musical authority of the time. Letter from Leopold to his wife, 27 March.

Sunday, I was honoured to visit H.E.M. the Count Pallavicini and to give him a letter of introduction from H.E. the Count of Firmian [Governor of Lombardy]: I had only just said that I was thinking of being in Rome during Holy Week, when he tells me that he wanted to try and organise something for the day after to have the pleasure of listening to this young extraordinary virtuoso and to obtain the same pleasure for the high-ranking nobles of the city. I do not want to start talking about all the circumstances when H.E. had us driven or placed his servants at our disposal, but only to let you know that close to 150 people of the highest nobility were present.[...] the famous Father Martini was also invited and, although he never attends any concerts, nontheless, he came. The concert started about half past seven and lasted until half past eleven, for the nobility would not leave.

Father Martini, the highest musical authority in Italy in the 18th century, who proved to be extremely benevolent towards little Wolfgang.

London
The origins of a symphonist

Mozart only visited London the once, and this was in his childhood. Accompanied by his parents and sister, he arrived in London from Paris on 23 April 1764 and left again for Holland, fifteen months later, on 24 July 1765. He was then a little more than nine years old. Leopold had planned a much shorter visit, but no doubt was unaware of the musical richness which would keep him in England. As early as 27 April, the entire Mozart family visited King George III and Queen Sophie Charlotte at St. James Park, where the welcome was one of the most cordial, very different from the "icy-coldness of Versailles". The invitation was renewed on 19 May, and on that day, reports Leopold, "the King made Wolfgang play not only pieces by Wagenseil, but also by Bach, Abel and Handel." The Bach in point was clearly not Johann Sebastian, but his youngest son Johann Christian (1735-1782), an Italian by adoption, arriving in London in 1762 for only a few months in principle, but in practice for the remainder of his days. The meeting with Johann Christian Bach and his

music was one of the most influential in Mozart's career. As for Handel, who died in London only five years previously (in 1759), he was (and was to remain) King George III's favourite composer. On 5 June, Mozart and his sister gave their first public concert in London (Leopold would derive an appreciable profit from it), and on 29 June, Wolfgang took part in a charity concert, pandering to English taste by playing an organ concerto (in the style for which Handel had become famous), on the advice of his father. After five or six weeks spent in the quiet of Chelsea, on the banks of the Thames, the Mozarts came back to

London in October and were once again received at court. But that year, the season was delayed ("The nobility has not yet returned to town and Parliament, contrary to custom, will not meet until 10 January.") London is thus a dead city and the disappointments pile up. No concerts in sight. Leopold finally managed to organise one for 21 February 1765: the receipts are meager. There will be another on 13 May. This will be Wolfgang's last public appearance in England. The last weeks were nonetheless remarkable for some important events: magistrate Daines Barrington's report on the "extraordinary" musical knowledge of Wolfgang.

" A child of only eight years of age;" the examination of a piano with two keyboards that the instrument maker Burkhardt Tschudi was sending to the Prussian king; hommage paid to the small prodigy by the British Museum. Paradoxically, it was in London, that most mundane of cities, where after their return from Chelsea, the Mozarts would spend the musically least mundane weeks of their great European tour of 1763-1766. Italianisation reigned supreme, and Johann Christian Bach, the only member of the Bach dynasty to have visited the Peninsula, had become its regent in a very brilliant

Six
SONATES
pour le
CLAVECIN
qui peuvent se jouer avec
l'accompagnement de Violon ou Flaute
Traversiere
Très humblement dediées
A SA MAJESTÉ
CHARLOTTE
REINE de la GRANDE BRETAGNE
Composées par
I.G. WOLFGANG MOZART
Agé de huit Ans
Oeuvre III.
LONDON Printed for the Author and sold at his Lodging
att Mr Williamson in Thrift Street Soho

Left, Queen Sophie Charlotte. Born Princess of Mecklenburg-Strelitz, she remained very attached to her German fatherland, just like her husband George III of Hannover. Thus she received Wolfgang very cordially and he dedicated his last sonatas for piano and violin to her (on the right, the frontis piece from this collection). Below, Covent Garden where Mozart, heard the great Handel oratorios during his stay in London.

musical environment. Arriving in London in 1762 to produce operas at the King's Theatre, becoming music teacher to the royal children, he was preparing to launch public concerts by subscription with his childhood friend Carl Friedrich Abel (the famous Bach-Abel concerts, the first of which will take place on 23 January 1765). In 1763, he staged two operas in London, *Orione and Zanaida,* and his *Six Favourite Overtures* appeared in the same year, resembling the symphonies. In 1765, his Opus 3, *Six Symphonies* followed. The allegros in song by Johann Christian Bach, his obsession with melody, his sensuality created a strong impression on the young Mozart, who was to meet his friend Johann Christian again in Paris in 1778. And when he learned of his death in 1782, he made a reflection rare for him: "Bach is no more, what a loss to music!"

In 1765, *Six Sonatas for harpsichord with violin accompaniment* (K 10-15) dedicated to Queen Sophie Charlotte were presented by Mozart. There was also an aria for tenor (K 21). But what is more important is that this sojourn in London marks the beginning of his career as a symphonist. Several of the symphonies written or drafted in England seem to have been lost, and that in E flat K 18 is really by Abel (Opus 7 No. 6). Amongst the authentic symphonies available, only three were perhaps heard in public concert: that in E flat, K 16, in D, K 19 (although it survived on Dutch paper) and in F, K 19a.

MARC VIGNAL

M	T	W	T	F	S	S
1	2	3	4	5	6	7
8	9	10	11	12	13	14
15	16	17	18	19	20	21
22	23	24	25	26	27	28
29	30					

APRIL   14th **WEEK**

1 Monday
8
9
10
11
12
13
14
15
16
17
18
19
20

1784 Vienna. Mozart is tireless: in one month he has taken part in more than twenty concerts.

2 Tuesday
8
9
10
11
12
13
14
15
16
17
18
19
20

1789 Impoverishment is a chronic sickness in the Mozart household. Still in desperate straits, Mozart signs a promissory note to Franz Hofdemel, husband of one of his pupils.

3 Wednesday
8
9
10
11
12
13
14
15
16
17
18
19
20

1781 The success Mozart received during a concert in Vienna upsets Colloredo, who wants to send him back to Salzburg. Mozart thinks of leaving the Prince Archbishop's service and confides in his father.

4 Thursday
8
9
10
11
12
13
14
15
16
17
18
19
20

1787 Whilst Constance begins another pregnancy. Mozart learns of his father's illness.

5 Friday
8
9
10
11
12
13
14
15
16
17
18
19
20

1778 Wolfgang meets the composer Gossec in Paris, through whom he makes contact with Parisian masonic circles.

6 Saturday

8

9

10

11

12

13

14

15

16

17

18

19

20

1786 Mozart completes *The Marriage of Figaro* which he had to abandon for the whole of January to write *The Theatre Director*. Learning that he was composing a new opera, his rivals did not remain inactive and sought to make the enterprise fail.

7 Sunday

8

9

10

11

12

13

14

15

16

17

18

19

20

1770 Leopold and Wolfgang are sorry to leave Florence, where they have been so well received by the Grand Duke of Tuscany Leopold I. Indeed, they have to hurry if they are to arrive in Rome for Holy Week.

The Mozart family making music: Wolfgang and his sister at the keyboard, Leopold on the violin. On the wall a portrait of the mother who died in Paris in 1778.

4 April 1787, this is the last letter that Mozart sends to his father, who dies on 28 May, three weeks after the first performance in Vienna of "Don Giovanni."
I am now learning that you are indeed sick ! I do not have to tell you how impatiently I am hoping for a further reassurance from your own pen; and I am expecting it just as firmly - al though I am accustomed to always imagine the worst in any circumstances. As death (if you well believe such things) is the ultimate aim of our lives, a few years ago I accepted this true and best friend of mankind, so that not only is its image no longer frightening to me, but it is instead something more reassuring and consoling ! And I thank my God for having given me the happiness (you do understand me) of discovering this as the key to our true happiness. I will never sleep without thinking (as young as I am) that I may not be here tomorrow -and no-one who knows me can say that I have a sorrowful or sad nature. I thank my Creator every day for this happiness and sincerely wish the same for all my fellow men. [...], I am revealing my line of though on this subject, on the occasion of the sad loss of my excellent best friend the Count of Hatzfeld [...]; I do not pity him, but rather, and in a friendly way, myself and all those who knew him as well as I did.

M	T	W	T	F	S	S
1	2	3	4	5	6	7
8	9	10	11	12	13	14
15	16	17	18	19	20	21
22	23	24	25	26	27	28
29	30					

APRIL 15th WEEK

8 Monday

8
9
10
11
12
13
14
15
16
17
18
19
20

1787 A sixteen-year-old musician arrives in Vienna, carrying letters of introduction to Mozart: Beethoven.

9 Tuesday

8
9
10
11
12
13
14
15
16
17
18
19
20

1782 Rumours are rife in Vienna that Joseph II will soon take Mozart into his service. "If the Emperor wants me, he will have to pay me" declares the interested party.

10 Wednesday

8
9
10
11
12
13
14
15
16
17
18
19
20

1764 The Mozarts leave Paris for England, where the English scholars who are making up a report on infant prodigies are impatiently waiting to look into his case.

11 Thursday

8
9
10
11
12
13
14
15
16
17
18
19
20

1770 The Mozarts arrive in Rome and immediately hasten to Saint Peter's to hear mass. They return the next day to watch the office celebrated by the Sovereign Pontiff. Those present are hand-picked and the Swiss make an unrelenting barrier, but the imposing presence of Leopold bears down upon them; hearing them speak in German, they imagine that they are part of the papal party and let them pass.

12 Friday

8
9
10
11
12
13
14
15
16
17
18
19
20

1789 Mozart is on his way to Berlin, accompanied by Prince Lichnowsky. He has banked his hopes on Frederick-William II, successor to the Great Frederick, who is a great music lover and has been sympathetic towards him. After a short rest in Prague, they stop in Dresden, where he plays before the Court.

14 Sunday

8	
9	
10	
11	
12	
13	
14	
15	
16	
17	
18	
19	
20	

1775 To celebrate the journey through Salzburg of Archduke Maximillian Franz, Colloredo commissions a "Theatrical festivity" from Mozart, *Il re pastore*.

13 Saturday

8
9
10
11
12
13
14
15
16
17
18
19
20

1791 Vienna. Once more Mozart find himself obliged to appeal to Puchberg's generosity. It is the ceaseless treadmill of loans and difficult repayment dates. Wolfgang and Constance have had to move home several times into progressively more modest appartments.

On 11 April 1770, in the Sistine Chapel, Mozart hears the "Miserere" for nine voices by Gregorio Allegri. Leopold Mozart to his wife from Rome, 14 April 1770. You have perhaps heard about the famous *Miserere*, so highly esteemed that the musicians of the choir are forbidden, on pain of excommunication, to leave with the smallest section of this piece, or to copy or communicate it to anyone ? Well, we already have it. Wolfgang has written it from memory and we would have sent it to Salzburg with this letter if we could have been present for its performance; but the way it is performed is worth more than the composition itself, and therefore, we will bring it home ourselves. As it is one of Rome's secrets, we do not want to entrust it to unknown hands *ut non incurremus mediate vel immediate in Censuram Ecclesiae* [so as not to incur, directly or indirectly, censure from the Church]. We have already made a thorough visit to the Saint Peter Basilica and we will not fail to visit what remains to be seen here. Tomorrow (God willing), we will see His Holiness pontificate. You cannot imagine the pride of the *abbate* here. Whoever has the slightest dealing with a cardinal conducts himself like a cardinal himself. And as the lowliest cardinal attending the *funciones* of the Pope has a *corteggio* of three or four coaches, filled with his chaplains, secretaries and valets, and they take over the whole square, I am happy at the thought of spending tomorrow amongst these proud gentlemen and leaving them in ignorance of our identity, for nowhere have we been presented.

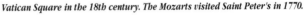

Vatican Square in the 18th century. The Mozarts visited Saint Peter's in 1770.

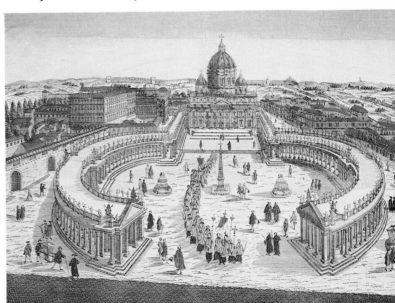

M	T	W	T	F	S	S
1	2	3	4	5	6	7
8	9	10	11	12	13	14
15	16	17	18	19	20	21
22	23	24	25	26	27	28
29	30					

APRIL   16th WEEK

15 Monday

8
9
10
11
12
13
14
15
16
17
18
19
20

1789 Mozart tries out Silberman's organ in Dresden.

16 Tuesday

8
9
10
11
12
13
14
15
16
17
18
19
20

1789 Still in Dresden, Mozart writes to Constance: "1) I ask you not to be sad; 2) to take care of your health; 3) not to go out alone on foot; 4) to be absolutely sure of my love..."

17 Wednesday

8
9
10
11
12
13
14
15
16
17
18
19
20

1766 The Mozarts reach Paris the day after a concert in Amsterdam (although any form of entertainment is rigorously prohibited in this period of Lent, exception was made for Wolfgang).

18 Thursday

8
9
10
11
12
13
14
15
16
17
18
19
20

1786 Set for the 28th, will the premiere of *The Mariage* be jeopardized because of the plots hatched by Salieri and Righini, who both hope to see their own opera performed before ? Salieri tries to discourage the performers by pretending that the arias are not singable.

19 Friday

8
9
10
11
12
13
14
15
16
17
18
19
20

1787 . Mozart confesses his anguish over the strings in the *Quintet in C*, K 515.

20 Saturday

8

9

10

11

12

13

14

15

16

17

18

19

20

1782 In Vienna, Mozart again meets the Baron van Swieten, rich lover and composer when in the mood, who tries to get him to share his admiration for Bach and Handel. Wolfgang takes part in musical meetings organised in his residence and dedicates his *Prelude* and *Fugue* K 394 to him.

21 Sunday

8

9

10

11

12

13

14

15

16

17

18

19

20

1779 Florence. "Manzuoli [the eunuch whom Mozart had known in London] is in process of negotiating with the Milanese to sing in my opera [*Mitridate*] and with this in mind he sang four or five arias for me; several of them mine that I was obliged to compose in Milan. I wanted them to know there that I was capable of writing an opera."

The organ of the church in Ulm. During the journey to Germany in 1789, Mozart often had chance to sit down at the keyboard. Such was the case in Dresden, where he had to compare himself to Hassler. And also in Leipzig, where he was moved to play the organ previously used by the great Johann Sebastian Bach. He had undertaken this journey to try and resolve his financial problems, seeing that Vienna offered him hardly any favourable prospects. Unfortunately, this long German tour did not match his expectations, and he obtained neither commissions nor employment. Frederick William II, in whom he had placed his hopes, already kept a number of musicians at his court, and he doubtless did not want to risk displeasing the Emperor in engaging one of his subjects.

On 15 April 1789, Mozart, who was travelling in Germany with his pupil Charles von Lichnowsky, arrives in Dresden, where he compares himself to Johann Wilhelm Hassler. He tells of this musical contest to his wife in a letter dated 16 April.

You know that here there is a certain *Hassler* (organist from Erfurt)- he is the pupil of a pupil of Bach. His *strength* is the *organ* and the keyboard (clavichord). Here the people believe, as I come from Vienna, that I do not know this style and way of playing. Thus I am seated at the organ and playing. Prince Lichnowsky (who knows Hassler well) took much trouble to convince him also to play - Hassler's strength at the organ lies in the footplay, but as here, the pedal boards are graduated, this is not such a great art; he has simply learned by heart the harmonies and modulations of old Sebastian Bach, and is not in a position to correctly develop a fugue -his playing is not *solid* -, and he is hence far from being an Albrechtsberger [famous organist at the Viennese Court]. After that, it was decided to go once more to the Rusian envoy's for Hassler to hear me on the *forte piano* - he played too. And I find that Auernhammer (Mozart's pupil) also plays well on the *forte piano*. You may imagine how greatly has his prestige fallen.

M	T	W	T	F	S	S
1	2	3	4	5	6	7
8	9	10	11	12	13	14
15	16	17	18	19	20	21
22	23	24	25	26	27	28
29	30					

APRIL 17th WEEK

22 Monday
8

9

10

11

12

13

14

15

16

17

18

19

20

1775 Salzburg. A Fischietti serenade opens the festival given in honour of Maximillian Franz.

23 Tuesday
8

9

10

11

12

13

14

15

16

17

18

19

20

1764 The Mozarts reach London, after a crossing that leaves a bad memory. They will stay sixteen months in London.

24 Wednesday
8

9

10

11

12

13

14

15

16

17

18

19

20

1785 Vienna. During a banquet given by the Crowned Hope Lodge in honour of Ignatz von Born (the future model for Sarastro). Mozart conducts his *Die Maurer Freude cantata*.

25 Thursday
8

9

10

11

12

13

14

15

16

17

18

19

20

1789 Still accompanied by Prince Lichnowsky, Mozart arrives in Potsdam, their journey's end. But despite all his admiration for Mozart, King Frederick William II of Prussia will not offer him any proposals.

26 Friday
8

9

10

11

12

13

14

15

16

17

18

19

20

1778 Paris. Only just finished, the *Sinfonia Concertante for Flute, Oboe, Horn and Bassoon* is given to Le Gros. It will however not be played at the Spiritual Concerts and Mozart will adapt it thereafter to include the clarinet.

27 Saturday

8

9

10

11

12

13

14

15

16

17

18

19

20

1764 London. George II and the Queen receive the Mozarts warmly at Court. The Queen's music professor, Johann Christian Bach (the last of the sons of Johann Sebastian), will form a liking for Wolfgang.

28 Sunday

8

9

10

11

12

13

14

15

16

17

18

19

20

1781 The storm erupts between Colloredo and Wolfgang the "insolent" servant who persists in wanting to leave Vienna.

Vauxhall Gardens in London. Open air concerts were performed there in summer.

On 22 April 1764, the Mozart family crosses the Channel and arrives in England. Leopold Mozart to Johann Lorenz Hagenauer in Salzburg. London, 25 April 1764.

We have, God be praised, crossed the Maxglan stream [a stream in the Salzburg suburbs] without hindrance, but this has not been S.V. [*salva venia* = beg your pardon] without vomiting; but I was the one most affected. This has prevented us from taking emetics; and we are, thanks be to God, all in good health. But he who has too much money has only to undertake a journey from Paris to London, it would not fail to lighten his purse. We were honoured to pay 4 louis d'or at Calais, although we took a meal not at the inn but with the *Procurator for the King and the Admiralty*, where we also left our carriage. As soon as you arrive in Dover, it is even worse; and when you leave the boat you are assailed by 30 or 40 people who are all at your service and wanting at all cost to take the luggage from the hands of your own servants to carry them to the inn, and then you have to pay what they ask. I had to pay 3 louis d'or for the crossing, for I had taken a special boat for which you pay 5 louis d'or, and took with us four other friends who each paid me half a louis d'or. Indeed there were 14 people on the ferry; and as there are only 10 to 12 beds on each boat, it is very unpleasant to live close to so many people sometimes with terrible seasickness.

M	T	W	T	F	S	S
1	2	3	4	5	6	7
8	9	10	11	12	13	14
15	16	17	18	19	20	21
22	23	24	25	26	27	28
29	30					

APRIL 18th **WEEK**

MAY

29 Monday
8
9
10
11
12
13
14
15
16
17
18
19
20

1772 Wolfgang writes a theatrical serenade, *Il sogno di Scipione*, for the enthronement of Colloredo.

30 Tuesday
8
9
10
11
12
13
14
15
16
17
18
19
20

1788 Repeat of *Don Giovanni* in Vienna. This time Mozart has added three pieces, an aria for Ottavio, one for Elvira and a duet for Leporello and Zerlina.

1 Wednesday
8
9
10
11
12
13
14
15
16
17
18
19
20

1778 Wolfgang, who was expecting so much from the Duchess of Bourbon's patronage, has first of all to conquer the Parisian salon of Mme de Chabot. After waiting in a stone-cold room, he will have to play to the "chairs, tables and walls", such is the indifference of the people.

2 Thursday
8
9
10
11
12
13
14
15
16
17
18
19
20

1786 Vienna. The day after the Burgtheater premiere of *The Marriage*, when all the pieces were given an ovation, success seems to be at his feet. Yet, the work will founder after nine performances.

3 Friday
8
9
10
11
12
13
14
15
16
17
18
19
20

1773 Salzburg. *Concertone for 2 violins in C major* K 202.

4 Saturday	**5** Sunday
8	8
9	9
10	10
11	11
12	12
13	13
14	14
15	15
16	16
17	17
18	18
19	19
20	20

1774 Salzburg. *Symphony n° 30 in D major* K 202.

There has to be one day in the life of Mozart when nothing happens !

Left, the poster for the first performance of "The Marriage of Figaro" at the Burgtheater, Vienna, 1 May 1786. Below, design of the Countess's costume. Beaumarchais' play had incurred the wrath of the censor and Mozart and his librettist had to dilute the social and political satire.

1 May 1986, first performance in Vienna of "The Marriage of Figaro" (K 492). Leopold Mozart to his daughter, 28 April 1786.

Your brother's opera, *Le Nozze di Figaro*, is being staged today the 28th, for the first time [it was, in fact, 1 May]. He will be lucky it manages to be a success as I know that there are some extraordinary *cabales* against him. *Salieri* and his entire following will not spare themselves to move heaven and earth. Mr and Mrs Duschek [Mozart's friends from Prague] told me that there are so many *cabales* against him because he is highly regarded for his *talent* and virtuosity. Count Johann Karl Zinzendorf notes [in French] in his diary after the performance: 1 of May 7 p.m. at the opera for the *Nozze di Figaro*, Da Ponte's poetry, the music of Mozardt [sic]. Louise in our box, the opera was a bore ...

Munich
A missed opportunity

To escape Salzburg, which he considered a prison, the young Mozart could travel in two directions: east to Vienna, attracted by the great figure of Haydn, or north-west to Mannheim, rendered brilliant by the best orchestra in Europe, founded by Johann Stamitz and maintained in its glory by Christian Cannabich. But on the road from Mannheim, not very far away (120 kilometers, or eighteen hours by coach) was another center of attraction: Munich. Mozart ended by choosing Vienna when, in May 1781, he broke with Archbishop Colloredo. But he had previously on several occasions sought to find a stable situation with the Prince Elector of Bavaria. Maximilian III (1727-1777) was a good musician, playing the viola da gamba and even attempting composition. In 1753, he had built an Opera House, one of the most beautiful in the world (where *Idomeneo* was created). Very favourable to Mozart, he nevertheless found nothing to offer him. Mozart travelled to Munich six times. Leopold had taken the six-year old child to the

carnaval in 1762, and had him play before the prince. The next year, on the long trip to Paris and London, he stopped in Munich on 12 June. The little prodigy astonished the court, received a reward, and was invited to return. He was not to do so for twelve years, but when he did, it was for a serious motive: the prince had ordered an *opera buffa* for the carnaval of 1775. The premiere of *La Finta Giardiniera* was held on 13 January, with a brilliant success. Leopold, who accompanied his son, recounts that Colloredo paid a visit to his illustrious neighbour, but missed the first performance of

Above, the Market Place in Munich in the 18th century. In 1774, the Prince of the Palatinate in Bavaria, Maximilian III, begged Colloredo to «loan» him Mozart, from whom he wished to order an opera for the carnaval season of 1775. The opera would be «La Finta Giardiniera.»

the opera. When Maximilian congratulated him on his Konzertmeister, «he was so much put out,» writes Leopold, that he answered only with a slight nod, and a shrug of the shoulders». There must have been some feeling of jealousy, since rumours were current that Mozart might soon enter the service of the prince… Munich was a necessary stopping place on the road to Paris. This time, in 1777, Mozart was alone with his

mother. Leopold, in his letters, followed his son closely: he should assert himself with opera intendant Count Seeau; if possible, he should speak to the prince. This became a reality on 29 September, and about the short interview, which proved fruitless, Mozart reports: «I am sorry for it, my dear child, but there are no vacancies at this time». In reality, the prince did not wish to take into his service a musician who had broken his

ban with a neighbouring prince. Upon his departure from Munich, Mozart stopped at Mannheim, where, to the great despair of Leopold, who saw through his evasions, he lingered from 30 October 1777 to March 1778. At first, this was because he had found excellent musicians there: Cannabich, Wendling, and Raaf. But above all, he had fallen upon the large Weber family, and he was madly taken with Aloysia. Upon his return from Paris, he was to delay at Mannheim no longer, and took himself off for Munich, because he had learned that his Aloysia had

been offered a position at the Opera. But at Christmas, he suffered a cruel rebuke at the hands of the young beauty, and resolved to return to Salzburg. There, he champed at the bit until, in 1780, he received a new command from the court of Munich. This was a beautiful opportunity for him to flee Salzburg for a moment. Maximilian, who had died on 30 December 1777, had been replaced by Elector of the Palatinate Charles Theodore, a protégé of the King of Prussia. In the meantime, the orchestra from Mannheim had moved to Munich, along with the excellent singers (Windling, mother and daughter, Raaf) who interpreted *Idomeneo* on 29 January 1781. Mozart remained at Munich for an unduly long time, and Colloredo called upon him to rejoin him forward, Mozart had no more reason to return to Munich. He had not long before endeavoured to enter the service of Maximilian, but

above all it was to escape from Salzburg, its Archbishop and obtuse public. We know that we are destined to pay dearly for the independence he gained by moving to Vienna. Should we regret that he found no opening in Munich? The situation there would have been unworthy of him, and he would soon have suffered from a confinement just as narrow as that of Salzburg. He attempted without success to find a position at the Prussian court; turned down the enthusiastic call from Prague; and renounced the move to London, perhaps the one place in the world where he would have been truly appreciated, as were Handel and Haydn (though Haydn himself felt homesick for Vienna, where he returned in 1796). Vienna was, after all, the only city Mozart liked, despite its ingratitude, and he was perhaps acquiring fame and fortune with the *Magic Flute* when he died.

JEAN VICTOR HOCQUARD

M	T	W	T	F	S	S
		1	2	3	4	5
6	7	8	9	10	11	12
13	14	15	16	17	18	19
20	21	22	23	24	25	26
27	28	29	30	31		

MAY °   19th WEEK

6 Monday

8

9

10

11

12

13

14

15

16

17

18

19

20

1770 The Mozarts' visit to Rome is coming to an end. Leopold writes to his wife, Wolfgang has ."growp up a little".

7 Tuesday

8

9

10

11

12

13

14

15

16

17

18

19

20

1783 Mozart makes the acquaintance in Vienna of a certain Father Da Ponte, to whom he promises his next libretto, as soon as a commission from Salieri has been fulfilled.

8 Wednesday

8

9

10

11

12

13

14

15

16

17

18

19

20

1782 Supported by Baron van Swieten, Mozart joined forces with a man called Martin to organise the Concert of the Dilettantes, a dominical event for music lovers, but also one of the very first associations for public concerts.

9 Thursday

8

9

10

11

12

13

14

15

16

17

18

19

20

1781 The break with Colloredo is final, "Today, my hapiness begins", writes Wolfgang on the evening of the violent scene in which he came into conflict with the Prince Archbishop. Such is the shock of this long-desired freedom that he falls ill...

10 Friday

8

9

10

11

12

13

14

15

16

17

18

19

20

1791 Mozart is appointed Assistant Choirmaster at Saint- Etienne Hoffman, in reply to a request sent to the Viennese City Council.

11 Saturday

8

9

10

11

12

13

14

15

16

17

18

19

20

1790 Like the previous year, Constance has had to leave Vienna to take the waters at Baden, for her health has been affected by difficult pregnancies in close succession. Wolfgang begs her to take her health more seriously.

12 Sunday

8

9

10

11

12

13

14

15

16

17

18

19

20

1789 Mozart and Prince Lichnowsky have left Berlin for Leipzig, where they meet Josepha Duschek again. Irritated by the lack of success of his endeavours, Wolfgang quarrels with his travelling companion, who wants to go back home immediately. Lichnowsky will depart alone, leaving Mozart to find his own means of subsistence and even making him hand over one hundred florins.

The Prince Archbishop Colloredo, who succeeded the debonair Sigmund von Strattenbach in Vienna.

9 May 1781, in Vienna, Mozart clashes very violently with the Prince Archbishop Colloredo. He describes the scene to his father.

When I arrived over there, the menservants told me that the Archbishop wanted to give me a *message* - I asked if it was urgent, and they said yes, it was very important. Well I am sorry but I will not able to have the honour to serve His Grace the Prince until Saturday; [...] When I stood before him, the first thing said was: - *Arch.* So, when is this boy leaving ? - *Myself:* I wanted to leave tonight, but there is no more room. [...] It was impossible to answer, he went on like a bush fire. [...] At last, even though my blood was boiling over, I say - Your Honour is not then satisfied with me ? -What, you dare threaten me, cretin (yes, cretin !) - There is the door, over there, I do not want to have any more to do with such a despicable brat. At last I say - Nor I with you ! In that case, let him go. And as I leave - So be it; tomorrow, you will receive my resignation in writing.

```
      M  T  W  T  F  S  S
            1  2  3  4  5
      6  7  8  9  10 11 12
      13 14 15 16 17 18 19
      20 21 22 23 24 25 26
      27 28 29 30 31
```

MAY   20th WEEK

17 Friday
8

9

10

11

12

13

14

15

16

17

18

19

20

1789 Mozart in turn leaves Leipzig, but, rather than go back to Vienna, he returns to Berlin where *Die Entführung aus dem Serail* was to be performed.

16 Thursday
8

9

10

11

12

13

14

15

16

17

18

19

20

1787 *Quintet for strings* in G minor (K 516). An unspeakable melancholy emanates, as though the first quintet, composed a month earlier, was not enough to cast out Mozart's anguish.

15 Wednesday
8

9

10

11

12

13

14

15

16

17

18

19

20

1770 Leopold and Wolfgang discover Naples, which they think is very noisy. But they are ecstatic about the beauties of Heraculanum and Pompei, which were only recently unearthed.

14 Tuesday
8

9

10

11

12

13

14

15

16

17

18

19

20

1778 A position as organist at Versailles is offered to Mozart. Leopold urges him to accept, but he does not reply to the offer.

13 Monday
8

9

10

11

12

13

14

15

16

17

18

19

20

1767 Fist performance at the University of Salzburg of a comedy in Latin by Wolfgang, *Apollo and Hyacinthus*.

19 Sunday

8

9

10

11

12

13

14

15

16

17

18

19

20

1789 Berlin. Mozart goes incognito to the theatre where *Die Entführung* is being performed. When he protests noisily at a wrong note from one of the singers, he is recognised. He is borne triumphantly onto the stage.

18 Saturday

8

9

10

11

12

13

14

15

16

17

18

19

20

1770 Naples. First visit to Portici, seat of the Court, to Minister of State Janucci. In the evening, the Mozarts call on Lord Hamilton, English Ambassador.

14 May 1770, Leopold Mozart and his son discover Naples, where they will stay until the end of June, and Vesuvius. They frequent the home of the English Ambassador, Lord Hamilton. Wolfgang writes on 19 May to his sister Nannerl, still in Salzburg.

We have seen the King and the Queen [Ferdinand IV, Sovereign of Naples and Maria-Caroline, born in Austria, daughter of Maria-Theresa] at the mass in the chapel to the court, in Portici. We have also seen Vesuvius; Naples is a beautiful city, but densely populated like Vienna and Paris. Between London and Naples, for the impertinence of the people, I am not sure that Naples is worse than London. Here the people, the *lazzaroni,* have their own leader or governor who every month receives 25 *ducati d'argento* from the King, simply for keeping order amongst the *lazzaroni.*

On 16 juin , he adds: " I am still alive and am as happy as ever, and am enjoying the travelling. I even went into the Merditerraneum Sea [one of those French scatological plays on words which Mozart has a habit of making]".

Popular festival in Naples, by Pietro Fabris. Leopold and Wolfgang were already famous in Naples even before their arrival, and the whole city, from the aristocratic palaces to the alleyways of the city, gave them a warm welcome.

M	T	W	T	F	S	S
			1	2	3	4	5
6	7	8	9	10	11	12
13	14	15	16	17	18	19
20	21	22	23	24	25	26
27	28	29	30	31		

MAY   21th WEEK

20 Monday

8
9
10
11
12
13
14
15
16
17
18
19
20

1785 Vienna *Fantasy for piano in C major* dedicated by Mozart to his pupil Theresa von Trattner.

21 Tuesday

8
9
10
11
12
13
14
15
16
17
18
19
20

1783 Mozart, who must soon visit his father in Salzburg, is worried about Colloredo's intentions towards him. Could the Prince Archbishop not have him arrested?

22 Wednesday

8
9
10
11
12
13
14
15
16
17
18
19
20

1770 Naples. Leopold Mozart to his wife: "Yesterday, the Marchioness Janucci, wife of the Prime Minister, sent me her major-domo to tell me that he was at my orders to drive us wherever we wanted and to show us the sights of Naples."

23 Thursday

8
9
10
11
12
13
14
15
16
17
18
19
20

1791 Vienna. *Quintet for glass harmonica, flute, oboe, viola and violoncello, K 617*, written by Mozart for the attention of a young blind virtuoso, Marianne Kirchgassner.

24 Friday

8
9
10
11
12
13
14
15
16
17
18
19
20

1789 Writting to Constance, Mozart confesse to her that his German tour has been a total failure. On the 26th, he will leave Berlin to return to Vienna: "My darling little wife, my return home will have to please you more than the money I bring you."

25 Saturday

8

9

10

11

12

13

14

15

16

17

18

19

20

1782 "Our first concert in the Augarten is tomorrow... Tonight, we have the rehearsal. There will be one sinfonia from van Swieten and one from me."

26 Sunday

8

9

10

11

12

13

14

15

16

17

18

19

20

1781 Leopold, troubled by the break with Colloredo, would like to have the son who is evading him return to Salzburg. As for Wolfgang, he tries to convince him of the need to stay in Vienna, where Stephanie has promised him another libretto after the abondonment of *Zaide*.

On 26 May 1782, the first Concert for the Dilettantes, organised by Mozart, takes place in the Augarten, Vienna. A letter to his father, on 8 May.

There will be music at the Augarten every Sunday this summer - a man named Martin staged a Concert for Dilettantes this winter [...] - Here, is a multitude of dilettantes, some even very good, as many women as men. But this did not seem very well organised to me. This Martin has now received, by order of Emperor, with an assurance of his extreme goodwill, authorisation to stage twelve concerts in the Augarten. [...]. The subscription for the whole summer costs 2 ducats. You will not then be surprised that we will have sufficient subscribers, all the more because I take care of this, and am thus an associate. Suppose we have only a hundred subscribers, each of us will receive 300 florins profit, even if the expenses rise to 200 florins, which they would not.

On 29 May 1782, Mozart is gratified to announce a success.

The first Concert for Dilettantes has gone well. Archduke Maximilian was present; as were Countess Thun, Wallenstein and Baron van Swieten...

The Augarten gardens in Vienna. The Concerts for Dilettantes were held here.

M	T	W	T	F	S	S
		1	2	3	4	5
6	7	8	9	10	11	12
13	14	15	16	17	18	19
20	21	22	23	24	25	26
27	28	29	30	31		

MAY 22th **WEEK**

27 Monday
8
9
10
11
12
13
14
15
16
17
18
19
20

1783 To obtain his parts, Leitgeb the horn player has to bend to Mozart's whims.

28 Tuesday
8
9
10
11
12
13
14
15
16
17
18
19
20

1787 Even though he seemed to be getting better, Leopold dies suddenly.

29 Wednesday
8
9
10
11
12
13
14
15
16
17
18
19
20

1778 Paris is much changed. The city wich previously welcomed the young prodigy with open arms now refuses to have anything to do with him. "I am, thank God, superficially very well. And yet can find neither rhyme nor reason in anything... I cannot find real joy anywhere."

30 Thursday
8
9
10
11
12
13
14
15
16
17
18
19
20

1783 Mozart offers the third act of *Die Entführung aus dem Serail* to Countess Thun, a few days before the start of rehearsals.

31 Friday
8
9
10
11
12
13
14
15
16
17
18
19
20

1766 The Mozarts are in Paris again. They are received twice at Versailles, visit the Royal Palace where the Duke of Orlean's daughter "takes the liberty of offering a little rondo to Wolfgang", and they attend the Prince de Conti's receptions.

	8
	9
0	10
1	11
2	12
3	13
4	14
5	15
6	16
7	17
8	18
9	19
20	20

1781 Regarding Colloredo whom he considers arrogant, Wolfgang writes "I effectively do as he expects; I do unto others as they do unto me - if I see that someone despises me and does not much care for me, I can be as proud as a monkey."

1788 An increasingly catastrophic financial position forces Mozart to move home to the suburbs of Vienna. He appeals to the generosity of Puchberg, his brother in freemasonry.

28 May 1787, Leopold Mozart dies in Strasbourg. Mozart gives the sad news to his friend Gottfried von Jacquin in Vienna.

I have to tell you that on my arrival home today, I learned the sad news of the death of my excellent father - you can imagine the state I am in !

On 2 June next, he writes to his sister in St. Gilgen.

You can well imagine my grief caused by the sad news of the brutal death of our dear father, since the loss is the same for both of us. As it is absolutely impossible for me to leave Vienna now [...] to settle the inheritance from our blessed father, I confirm that I fully share your opinion regarding a public sale; before making my choice, I am awaiting an inventory of the effects. [...] I would ask you to arrange to send our good friend Ippold the enclosed letter; as he has so often proved his attachment to our family, I hope that he will do me the favour of representing me personally in the necessary procedures. Farewell, my darling sister ! Forever your...

... faithful brother. W. A. Mozart

Portrait of Leopold Mozart by Jacobs Andreas Friedrich. Mozart did not show an excess of sorrow on the death of his father.

CONVENIT IGITUR --- IN GESTU NEC VENUSTATEM CONSPICUAM, NEC TURPITU- DINEM ESSE, NE AUT HISTRIONES AUT OPERARII VIDEAMUR ESSE

Italy
1769-1771
A Musician loved by the Gods

Leopold Mozart had just celebrated his fiftieth birthday when, on 13 December 1769, he decided to leave Salzburg and depart on the conquest of Italy with his son Wolfgang, at that time nearing his fourteenth birthday. Father Mozart wished to exhibit the child prodigy in the Peninsula with the help of a letter of introduction from the powerful Count Firmian. In additions, he hoped to sign several contracts for the years to come. For the young Wolfgang, this major experience had become indispensable. Writing arias in Italian on the models of the Neapolitan and Venetian schools since childhood, he needed this direct contact with a culture which presided over the future of the musical intelligentsia of Europe. Beginning on 22 December, Wolfgang announced his enthusiasm to his sister. Upon his arrival at Bolzano, a first meeting with the violinist Anton Kurzweil awaited him. The trip thereafter was to be a series of receptions, concerts, and of course, meetings, the influence of which would be later reflected in his musical production. Letters often indicated the titles of operas he attended in the various Italian theatres: *Ruggero* by Pietro Guglielmi (in Verona on 6 January), *La Clemenza di Tito* by Hasse himself (in Cremona on the 22nd of the same month), etc. After a concert in which everything was done to put the little genius in his best light, the Mantua Gazette spoke straightforwardly of the «musical miracle». Father Leopold did not miss any occasion, and regularly pointed out Wolfgang's success to the German press. The stay in Milan was of principal importance: Mozart wrote the concert air *Misero se tu non si*, met Niccolo Piccinni after the main performance of *Cesare in Egitto* (2 february), and, during the course of a glittering evening in the presence of the entire Milanese nobility, the Belgioioso, Borromeo, Beccaria families, he closed his first contract on 12 March: an opera for 1770-1771, with the completion of *Fra cento affani, Per pietà bell'idolo mio, Per quel paterno amplesso*, and the admirable *Misero me, misero pargoletto..* In Bologna, on 26 March, he succeeded in charming the venerable Father Martini and made the acquaintance of the legendary Farinelli, the most dazzling castrato singer of the eighteenth century. At Florence, on 1 April, he was

The libretto of this "Mitridate re di Ponto" was very freely inspired by the tragedy by Racine.

received by Archduke Leopold at the Pitti palace. At Rome, where he arrived on the 11th, he was dazzled by the Allegri's *Miserere*, heard in the Sistine Chapel. He immediately transcribed it without missing a note, as if he had photographed the score. Once again, the nobility reserved the warmest welcome for him; one reception succeeded another, with Prince Chigi, Princess Barberini, and Duke Odescalchi, all wishing to view the amazing prodigy at close quarters. On 8 May, they departed for Naples; after stopovers at Lake Albano and Capua, Leopold and his son made their entry on the 14th into the European capital of music. While writing: «Italy is the country of sleep; here I always want to go to sleep»,

Wolfgang burst forth with activity. He discovered Di Majo and Jommelli, whose *Armida abbandonata* appeared to him «too seria and too all'antica». After leaving a memorable concert at the della Pietà conservatory, Abbey Galliani wrote to Madame d'Epinay at Paris: «I believe I wrote to you that the little Mosar (sic) is here, and that he is less of a miracle, although he is always the same miracle, but he will never be anything but a miracle, and that's all». The second stay in Rome (26 June-10 July) was the pretext for even more prestigious receptions: by Pope Clement XIV at the Quirinale Palace and Santa Maria Maggiore, Wolfgang received the most flattering awards. After the trip to the Marches, in Umbria and

Above, the interior of the San Carlo Theatre in Naples. Opposite, Johann Adolf Hasse, the most italianized German musician of the 18th century.

in Romagna (Spoleto, Terni, Coreto, Ancona, Rimini, etc.) he returned to Bologna on 27 July, and read the libretto *Mitridate re di Ponto* for the first time, the recitatifs of which he began to put to music on 29 September. In Bologna, Mozart had little time at his disposal, concerts at San Petronio and San Domenico alternated with daily lessons with Father Martini. The rehearsals of *Mitridate* only began on 8 December at the Teatro Ducale of Milan. Upon the 26th of that month, the premiere inspired delirious excitement before an audience won over in advance. For twenty-two nights, all of Milan thronged to applaud the prodigy. Wolfgang could not leave Italy without promising to return with a new opera. He left Milan on 4 February, and after a stay in Venice, returned to Salzburg on 28 March. His first Italian trip had lasted more than fifteen months.

SERGIO SEGALINI

M	T	W	T	F	S	S
					1	2
3	4	5	6	7	8	9
10	11	12	13	14	15	16
17	18	19	20	21	22	23
24	25	26	27	28	29	30

JUNE 23rd WEEK

3 Monday
8
9
10
11
12
13
14
15
16
17
18
19
20

1786 Vienna. *Quartet N°. 2 for piano and strings in E flat major, K 493.*

4 Tuesday
8
9
10
11
12
13
14
15
16
17
18
19
20

1774 Salzburg. *Concerto for bassoon in B flat major K 191.*

5 Wednesday
8
9
10
11
12
13
14
15
16
17
18
19
20

1764 London. The Mozart children give their first public concert. In spite of the advanced season, Leopold reckons on 100 guineas profit.

6 Thursday
8
9
10
11
12
13
14
15
16
17
18
19
20

1791 Alone in Vienna - Constance is in Baden -, Mozart is slaving away on *The Magic Flute.*

7 Friday
8
9
10
11
12
13
14
15
16
17
18
19
20

1790 For reasons of economy, Mozart leaves Vienna and rejoins his wife Constance in Baden.

9 Sunday

8

9

10

11

12

13

14

15

16

17

18

19

20

1763 Leopold who has obtained leave of absence from the Prince Archbishop, leaves Salzburg with Anna Maria, Nannerl and Wolfgang. The journey will last for three years!

Saturday

8

9

10

11

12

13

14

15

16

17

18

19

20

1764 Leopold in London: "My daughter is the most skilful virtuoso in Europe even though she is only 12 years old, and my son, although he is only in his eighth year, knows as much as may be expected from a man of forty years".

On 8 June 1781, a kick in the behind from Count Karl Joseph Felix Arco brings the relationship between Mozart and the Prince Archbishop of Salzburg to a full stop. A humiliation that he relates to his father the following day.

This happens in the ante chambre - so I have no other means of unburdening myself and fleeing - not wanting to show a lack of the respect required in the princely appartments, even if Arco himself had forgotten it. [...]

Henceforth, I will not write any more about this whole business; and even if the arch. gave me a salary of 1,200 florins, I would not accept after such treatment - yet, I would have been quite open to persuasion ! If offered politely, not proudly nor vulgarly. [...] Does it concern him that I want to have my holiday ? And if he really wants of my best, let him seek to persuade me by argument - or let the matter drop. But he should not fire me as a "lout" or "good-for-nothing" , and not push me out of the door with a kick on the behind; but I was forgetting that it was perhaps on the prince's order.

Anonymous portrait of Mozart about twenty years of age.

M	T	W	T	F	S	S
					1	2
3	4	5	6	7	8	9
10	11	12	13	14	15	16
17	18	19	20	21	22	23
24	25	26	27	28	29	30

JUNE   24th WEEK

10 Monday

8

9

10

11

12

13

14

15

16

17

18

19

20

1770 In Naples, Leopold is distressed by "the squalor", the multitude of beggars, the unbelievable depravation .

11 Tuesday

8

9

10

11

12

13

14

15

16

17

18

19

20

1778 The Paris Opera puts up posters for a Noverre pantomine-ballet, *Les Petits Riens,* for which Mozart has written most of the pieces.

12 Wednesday

8

9

10

11

12

13

14

15

16

17

18

19

20

1778 So that he may be forgiven for having stolen the *Sinfonia Concertante,* Le Gros commissions another work for the Spiritual Concerts from Mozart. First performed on the 18th, this new symphony earns its writer his first success in the capital and will be called the *Paris Symphony.*

13 Thursday

8

9

10

11

12

13

14

15

16

17

18

19

20

1784 Concert in Vienna at the home of Ignaz von Ployer. Paisiello is present.

14 Friday

8

9

10

11

12

13

14

15

16

17

18

19

20

1775 Salzburg. *Violin Concerto No. 2 in D major* K 211.

15 Saturday

8

9

10

11

12

13

14

15

16

17

18

19

20

1778 Paris. Anna Maria begins to feel the first symptoms of the sickness which will carry her away.

16 Sunday

8

9

10

11

12

13

14

15

16

17

18

19

20

1787 Wolfgang and Nannerl amicably agree on the inheritance from Leopold. From now on, Nannerl will have hardly any contact with her brother.

Giovanni Paisiello, the Italian Music Ambassador in Vienna.

10 June 1763: Wolfgang, at the organ, is learning the pedal board. Leopold Mozart to Johann Lorenz Hagenauer in Salzburg. Wasserbourg, 11 June 1763.
Here is the latest news: to pass the time, we went to play the organ and I explained the pedal board to Wolferl. He immediately wanted to try it, *stante pede* [with the foot raised], he pushed back the stool, played a prelude first of all and used the pedal board as if he had already been practising for many months.
13 June 1784, concert at the home of Gottfried Ignaz von Ployer in Vienna. Giovanni Paisiello will be present, as Mozart writes to his father on 12 June.
Tomorrow, we will give a concert at Döbling at the country home of Mr Ployer the agent. Mlle Babette will play her new concerto in G - myself the quintet [K 452], and both of us the newest grand sonata for two pianos [K 448]. I will stop and take Paisiello in my carriage so he can hear my compositions and my pupil; if Maestro Sarti had not had to leave today, he would also have accompanied me - Sarti is an honest and worthy man!

M	T	W	T	F	S	S
					1	2
3	4	5	6	7	8	9
10	11	12	13	14	15	16
17	18	19	20	21	22	23
24	25	26	27	28	29	30

JUNE   25th WEEK

17 Monday

8
9
10
11
12
13
14
15
16
17
18
19
20

1783 Birth of Raymond in the Mozart home. *Quartet in D minor* K 421.

18 Tuesday

8
9
10
11
12
13
14
15
16
17
18
19
20

1791 Mozart composes the *Ave Verum* for the Celebration of the Eucharist, in Baden, where he has been with Constance for a few days.

19 Wednesday

8
9
10
11
12
13
14
15
16
17
18
19
20

1778 Anna Maria is confined to bed, suffering from violent headaches. She will never get up again.

20 Thursday

8
9
10
11
12
13
14
15
16
17
18
19
20

1781 Mozart envisages finally settling in Vienna, but he has no home since he left the Prince Archbishop. He goes to live with the Webers. Fridolin is dead and his widow keeps a boarding house. Aloysia left home six months ago to marry Joseph Lange.

21 Friday

8
9
10
11
12
13
14
15
16
17
18
19
20

1783 "Young Mozart [Raymond] is still very new and well and does everything abundantly, drinking, sleeping, crying, dribbling, shitting and the rest," writes the happy papa.

22 Saturday

8

9

10

11

12

13

14

15

16

17

18

19

20

1788 Vienna. *Trio for piano, violin and violincello in E major* K 542.

23 Sunday

8

9

10

11

12

13

14

15

16

17

18

19

20

1778 Anna Maria is getting worse. She loses her hearing. The doctor that Wolfgang sent for first of all is happy to prescribe rhubarb for her... Grimm will send her a more knowledge able practitioner, but it is already too late to check the illness.

18 June 1778, first performance of the Paris Symphony (K 297) at the Spiritual Concert in Paris. Mozart gives an account of this success to his father on 3 July.
I had to write a symphony for the opening of the Spiritual Concert. It was played on the day of the Celebration of the Eucharist and was given rapturous applause [...] I had been very frightened at rehearsal, for I have never in my life heard anything worse; you cannot imagine how they bungled and scraped through the symphony. [...] I would really have liked to rehearse yet one more time, but one always rehearses so many things at a time and there was not enough of it left, so I had to go to sleep with a troubled heart, illpleased and angry. The next day, I had even decided not to go to the Concert; but in the evening it turned out fine and I finally resolved to go, with the firm intention, if it was still just as bad [...], to go up to the *orchestra,* to *take* the violin from the hands of the *first violin,* Mr Lahoussaye, and to conduct it all myself. I was praying to God to allow it to go down well, since it is all being done in his greatest honour and glory and *ecce,* the symphony began, Raaf was sitting close to me; in the middle of the first *Allegro,* straightaway there is a passage that, I well knew, should please; the whole audience was enthusiastic - there was great *applause* -, but as I knew from writing it what *Effect* it would produce, I had reinserted it at the end - this began *da capo. L'Andante* also pleased, but the last *Allegro* even more so. As I had heard that here the last *Allegro* begin, like the first, with the instruments all together, and usually *unisono,* I had it start *piano* with the two violins on their own.

The Entrance to the Tuileries in the 18th century, by Leprince. The famous Spiritual Concerts took place in the Swiss Hall of the castle.

	M	T	W	T	F	S	S
						1	2
	3	4	5	6	7	8	9
	10	11	12	13	14	15	16
	17	18	19	20	21	22	23
	24	25	26	27	28	29	30

JUNE   26th WEEK

24 Monday
8
9
10
11
12
13
14
15
16
17
18
19
20

1771 Salzburg. Mozart writes an offertory for Saint John, *Inter nolos mulicrum.*

25 Tuesday
8
9
10
11
12
13
14
15
16
17
18
19
20

1770 Leopold and Wolfgang leave Naples for Rome.

26 Wednesday
8
9
10
11
12
13
14
15
16
17
18
19
20

1788 Vienna. *Symphony No. 39 in E flat major* K 543. First part of the admirable trilogy of the last great symphonies with *N°. 40 in G minor* (K 550) and *N°. 41 in C major* (K 551), called *the Jupiter.*

27 Thursday
8
9
10
11
12
13
14
15
16
17
18
19
20

1788 For the third time in less than a month, Mozart is obliged to ask Puchberg for a loan.

28 Friday
8
9
10
11
12
13
14
15
16
17
18
19
20

1764 Wolfgang takes part in a charity concert given at the Ranelagh in London. Leopold decided that his son would play "an organ concerto to show them over there that he is a good compatriot of the English".

29 Saturday

8

9

10

11

12

13

14

15

16

17

18

19

20

1788 Fate relentlessly pursues the Mozarts, for their little Theresa has just died. This is the third child that Wolfgang and Constance lose.

30 Sunday

8

9

10

11

12

13

14

15

16

17

18

19

20

1788 Paris. The unfortunate Anna Maria is given up for lost. Thus she is given the last sacraments.

This engraving of the time enables you to visualise what happened to Leopold and Wolfgang when their carriage "tipped them out" in the suburbs of Rome.

About 26 June 1770, close to Rome, the carriage which is transporting father and son Mozart has an accident. Leopold, injured in the leg, informs his wife on 30 June.

I was obliged to stay partly at home or only to limp about slowly, and could not then go pay my respects to the princes and cardinals. I hid the reason for this in my first letter, but as it seems to be getting better now, I can now tell you about the awful accident we have had. You know that two horses and one postillion make up three wild beasts. On the last stage to Rome, the postillion hit the horse which [...] reared up and [...] fell with force on its side. I held onto Wolfgang with one hand so that he would not be thrown out, but my right leg violently hit the central metal piece of the footboard which fell down giving me a wound the width of a finger over half of my tibia. [...] The day after, this took quite a dangerous turn for the leg was swollen. [...] But today as I am writing these lines, this is really getting better [...]. I have only used the white ointment and will stay with this. This has no doubt had to happen so that you would not have given me the ointment and the material for dressings for nothing; I am sorry I did not have more adhesive. Tell me in your next letter how it is made.

The second trip in the Peninsula was undertaken in rather better conditions than the first, the coach purchased in Italy proving superior in comfort to the first on all points. Wolfgang complained of the summer heat and lack of air. Leaving Salzburg on 13 August, he arrived in Milan on the 21st at seven o'clock in the evening. Eight days later, he received the libretto of *Ascanio in Alba*. At the same time, Hasse was rehearsing his

Ruggero, taken from a libretto by Metastasio.

The entire month of September was filled with composition, and the first fifteen days of October with rehearsals. On the 17th, the day after the premiere of *Ruggero*, celebrating the marriage of the Prince couple, *Ascanio in Alba* once more dazzled the Milanese aristocracy. The *Gazzetta di Milano* wrote a lengthy review and continued to speak of it until 13 November, wishing to mark the importance of the event. Indefatigably, Mozart continued to write: symphonies KV 92 and KV 112, the *Divertimento* in E flat KV 113, etc. He then undertook the return journey, hardly four months after his arrival. Leopold would have preferred to arrive in Salzburg earlier, but he did not wish to leave Milan without a firm engagement, something more than the mere promise of a contract for a new opera, intended for the following season.

In October 1777, Wolfgang again went on tour with his father; this third journey, even more glorious, would also be the last; Leopold did not succeed in obtaining a stable position for his son. This time,

wind, rain, and cold accompanied all their travels in the north: Trent, Rovereto, Verona and Brescia.

On 4 November at midday, the two finally arrived in Milan. Had Mozart already composed his *Lucio Silla?* Probably not, since the libretto by Giovanni di Gamerra had been sent to Vienna for Metastasio's approval, and was returned with a great many corrections, including the addition of an entire scene in the second act. Over the course of the five weeks in Milan, Wolfgang was able to write his new opera. The choice of singers was particularly fortunate. For Giunia, the Teatro Ducale engaged Anna de Amicis, a famous Neapolitan prima donna whom Mozart had applauded in Naples in *Armida abbandonata* by Jommelli. «She is our best friend», wrote Leopold. «She sings and plays like an angel». What is more, this great technician seemed perfectly satisfied with her role. At her side, brilliant in the role of Cecilio, was a castrato singer of great fame: Venanzio Rauzzini, trained in the Roman school. Mozart would have less luck with Bassano Morgnoni, a tenor at the church in Lodi

without any theatre experience. On the evening of the premiere, despite considerable efforts, his clumsiness was the cause of several regrettable stage accidents. The day after the 26 December premiere, no one seemed really satisfied. Nevertheless, the work was presented on twenty six successive nights with growing success. Everything seemed to favour a definitive stay in Italy for the Mozarts; during the entire month of January, Leopold waited with desperate excitement for a contract in Florence. On 9 January, writing

Opposite, Giovanni Paisiello (1740-1816), one of the most elegant representatives, with Cimarosa, of Neapolitan comic opera. He adapted Beaumarchais' «Barbiere di Siviglia».

to his wife, he declared: «I have no intention of leaving... we are absolutely eager to hear Paisiello's second opera». An opera which premiered upon 30 January: this *Sismano nel Mogol* permitted closer contact with the music of the Neapolitan composer. The divine Mozart probably did not doubt that upon his return to Salzburg on 13 March, after a seven-day journey, he would dedicate himself from that time forward to the comedy of the Parthenopean Gulf. After his experience in *opera seria alla tedesca*, his *italianità* would explode in *Cosi fan tutte*, *Don Giovanni* and *Le Nozze di Figaro*. The meeting with Da Ponte would be decisive. The tours in Italy would be, for him, only an emotion-filled memory, burdened with yearning.

SERGIO SEGALINI

Below, a view of Milan in the 18th century. Returning to Salzburg after their long Italian tour, Wolfgang and his father did not stay long. In the month of August 1771, they were back in Milan. Opposite, the manuscript of "Lucio Silla".

M	T	W	T	F	S	S
1	2	3	4	5	6	7
8	9	10	11	12	13	14
15	16	17	18	19	20	21
22	23	24	25	26	27	28
29	30	31				

JULY — 27th WEEK

1 Monday
8
9
10
11
12
13
14
15
16
17
18
19
20

1789 Constance is suffering from a foot infection. Once more, Mozarts turns to Puchberg.

2 Tuesday
8
9
10
11
12
13
14
15
16
17
18
19
20

1791 Constance, staying in Baden for a cure, is the object of Mozart's every attention: "Look after your health, for when you are not well, nothing will exist for me any more, and if you are well, everything is well with me".

3 Wednesday
9
10
11
12
13
14
15
16
17
18
19
20

1778 Anna Maria passes away in the evening. Wolfgang only speaks about illness to Leopold. But he will tell the truth to Father Bullinger, a family friend, asking him to prepare the family. On this day, he writes: "The impious, master rogue Voltaire is worn out, like a dog in other words, like a beast. Here are his wages".

4 Thursday
8
9
10
11
12
13
14
15
16
17
18
19
20

1778 Paris. Anna Maria is given a pauper's burial in the Saint Eustache Church in Paris.

5 Friday
8
9
10
11
12
13
14
15
16
17
18
19
20

1791 Concerned by Mozart's intellectual loneliness, Schikaneder has installed him in a little cottage close to the theatre where the musician leads a joyful life in the company of the actors.

6 Saturday

8

9

10

11

12

13

14

15

16

17

18

19

20

1765 In London, Mozart writes a sonata for four hands for Nannerl and himself. Leopold declares that this is the first of its kind, forgetting that Johann Christian Bach had done it before his son.

7 Sunday

8

9

10

11

12

13

14

15

16

17

18

19

20

1791 Mozart sends more notes to Constance, love letters full of tenderness, in which his lassitude is also revealed.

Anna Maria Pertl, Mozart's mother, who died in Paris in 1778

3 July 1778, in Paris, Mozart suffered the sorrow of losing his mother. That very night, he writes to Father Franz Joseph Bul linger, a family friend, to ask him to prepare his father to receive this sombre news.

Weep with me, my friend ! This has been the saddest day of my life - I am writing this to you at 2 o'clock in the morning. I still have to tell you: my mother, my dear mother is no more ! God has called her to Him. He wanted to have her, it was clear to me [...]. Imagine the worry, anguish and the cares that I have endured during these two weeks. She died without realising it. She had been continually delirious for the past three days, and today at 21 minutes past 5, she began her agony, immediately lost all sensation [...] I squeezed her hand, spoke to her, she did not see me, did not hear me and felt nothing. She remained like this for five hours until the moment she expired, at 21 minutes past 10. I now ask you only to do me the favour of very gently preparing my father to receive this sad news.

M	T	W	T	F	S	S
1	2	3	4	5	6	7
8	9	10	11	12	13	14
15	16	17	18	19	20	21
22	23	24	25	26	27	28
29	30	31				

JULY   28th **WEEK**

12 Friday

8

9

10

11

12

13

14

15

16

17

18

19

20

1789 Constance is gravely ill. The meager profits from the trip to Berlin have melted away. Mozart directs a request to the indulgent Puchberg. "Fate is hostile towards me , he writes, but only in Vienna."

11 Thursday

8

9

10

11

12

13

14

15

16

17

18

19

20

1791 Mozart returns from Baden accompanied by Constance.

10 Wednesday

8

9

10

11

12

13

14

15

16

17

18

19

20

1770 Rome. Promoted to the rank of Knight of the Golden Spur, Mozart has an audience with Pope Clement XIV.

9 Tuesday

8

9

10

11

12

13

14

15

16

17

18

19

20

1778 Wolfgang informs Leopold of the death of Anna Maria. He has already turned the page and is reminded again of his plans for marriage to Aloysia, a prospect to which his mother was even more hostile than his father.

8 Monday

8

9

10

11

12

13

14

15

16

17

18

19

20

1786 *Trio for piano, violin and violin-cello Nº. 3 in G major* K 496: Mozart tackles this style.

14 Sunday

8

9

10

11

12

13

14

15

16

17

18

19

20

1789 Whilst in Paris the extreme republicans capture the Bastille, Mozart, despairing of his situation, resolves to send his request to Puchberg.

13 Saturday

8

9

10

11

12

13

14

15

16

17

18

19

20

1781 Vienna. Rumours start to circulate regarding Wolfgang's relationship with the unmarried Weber daughters, since he lives under the same roof.

8 July 1770, returning to Rome from a visit to Naples, Wolfgang is received by Pope Clement XIV, who makes him a Knight of the Order of the Golden Spur, a much envied distinction, that Gluck also received. A very proud Leopold informs his wife of this event on 7 July.

What I wrote you recently on the subject of a cross of an order is true. I have also written today to His Highness the Prince [the Prince Archbishop of Salzburg, Schrattenbach] and have sent him the copy of the Papal brief. I have scarcely had time to copy it rather badly for H.H. the Prince, if not I would have copied it twice and sent it to you as well. It is the same order as Gluck's, it is entitled te *creamus auratae Militae Equitem*, etc., etc. He has to carry a fine golden cross sent to him, and you may imagine how much I laugh when I hear him called *Signor Cavaliere*. You know how one may still read, in the operata librettos printed by the Court of Vienna, dal *Sigr. Cavaliere* Gluck. This is proof that this order is recognised even at the imperial court. For this reason we will receive a copy of the Bulla Benedicti XIV. [...] Tomorrow, we have an audience with the Pope and Monday evening we will leave for Loreto [a very popular place of pilgrimage].

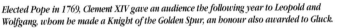

Elected Pope in 1769, Clement XIV gave an audience the following year to Leopold and Wolfgang, whom he made a Knight of the Golden Spur, an honour also awarded to Gluck.

M	T	W	T	F	S	S
1	2	3	4	5	6	7
8	9	10	11	12	13	14
15	16	17	18	19	20	21
22	23	24	25	26	27	28
29	30	31				

JULY   29th **WEEK**

15 Monday
8
9
10
11
12
13
14
15
16
17
18
19
20

1766 Paris. Grimm writes concerning the Mozarts: "If these children are to live, they will not stay in Salzburg."

16 Tuesday
8
9
10
11
12
13
14
15
16
17
18
19
20

1782 Vienna. Premiere of Die Entführung aus dem Serail. The new ideas included in this singspiel, which confer nobility on this kind of work, arouse contradictory opinions. But popular success is achieved.

17 Wednesday
8
9
10
11
12
13
14
15
16
17
18
19
20

1789 In desperate straits, Mozart swallows his pride and yet again begs his friend Puchberg: "In the name of God, I ask and implore you to grant me any immediate help you like, as well as advice and consolation."

18 Thursday
8
9
10
11
12
13
14
15
16
17
18
19
20

1778 Mozart to Leopold: "Does the word Paris give you the horrors ?"

19 Friday
8
9
10
11
12
13
14
15
16
17
18
19
20

1765 London. The British Museum pays hommage to Wolfgang by acquiring his Paris Sonatas as well as a portrait of the Mozart family, painted by Carmontelle.

20 Saturday

8

9

10

11

12

13

14

15

16

17

18

19

20

1778 Leopold to Wolfgang in reply to his letter of the 9th: "As for what you lead me to suppose in your letter after informing me of the sad news of the death of your dear mother whom I abandoned totally for your good, and for my peace of mind, this can hardly help to reassure me."

21 Sunday

8

9

10

11

12

13

14

15

16

17

18

19

20

1782 Haffner, Burgomaster of Salzburg, suddenly remembers Mozart and commissions a work from him. The *Haffner Symphony* will be completed on 7 August.

Leopold Mozart and his children, by Carmontelle. Subsequently, Leopold was to leave Nannerl in Salzburg, and she felt somewhat bitter about this.

On 18 July 1766, the Mozart children give a concert in the city of Dijon which is announced as follows.

By permission of His Serene Highness, His Eminence the Prince de Condé [Louis-Joseph of Bourbon] who will honour with his presence, the concert that Mr Mozart, Master of Music at the Chapel of the Prince, Archbishop of Salzburg, will be proud to give tomorrow, 18 July 1766.

A grand concert in the Town Hall,

in which his Son, aged 9 years and his daughter of 14, will perform Works on the Harpsichord composed by the greatest Masters. They will also perform Works for two Harpsichords, & Pieces on the same instrument for four hands.

He will sing an air he composed, & all the Overtures will be by this young Child, great Composer, who has never met his equal and has received admiration at the Courts of Versailles, Vienna and London. Amateurs, if they so wish, will be able to present him with Music, he can perform anything on sight. We start at eight o'clock. Entrance 3 francs.

M	T	W	T	F	S	S
1	2	3	4	5	6	7
8	9	10	11	12	13	14
15	16	17	18	19	20	21
22	23	24	25	26	27	28
29	30	31				

JULY 30th WEEK

22 Monday
8
9
10
11
12
13
14
15
16
17
18
19
20

1776 Salzburg, Mozart writes a serenade for the wedding of Elizabeth Haffner, daughter of the Burgomaster.

23 Tuesday
8
9
10
11
12
13
14
15
16
17
18
19
20

1770 As soon as he arrives in Bologna, where he is counting on spending the summer thanks to the hospitality offered by Count Pallavicini, Wolfgang receives the libretto for *Mitridate* from Milan and sets to work.

24 Wednesday
8
9
10
11
12
13
14
15
16
17
18
19
20

1765 The Mozarts leave London, planning to return to Salzburg via Milan and Venice. In fact, they will go to Holland.

25 Thursday
8
9
10
11
12
13
14
15
16
17
18
19
20

1781 Mozart is self-employed in Vienna, but after three months his situation hardly improves. He has only a few lessons to live on.

26 Friday
8
9
10
11
12
13
14
15
16
17
18
19
20

1791 Constance gives birth to her sixth child, Franz Xavier Wolfgang. Da Ponte, in disgrance since the death of Joseph II, leaves Vienna for London and suggests that Mozart accompany him. Wolfgang, who has to complete *The Magic Flute,* declines his offer.

27 Saturday

8

9

10

11

12

13

14

15

16

17

18

19

20

782 Exasperated by the scenes made by her mother who wishes to see her married as soon as possible, Constance runs away to find refuge with Baroness von Waldstätten. Wolfgang begs her father to give his consent to the marriage, claiming that the honour of the young girl is at stake.

28 Sunday

8

9

10

11

12

13

14

15

16

17

18

19

20

1778 Grimm to Leopold regarding Wolfgang: "He is too candid, not very active, too easy to attack, too little concerned with ways to make his fortune. To be noticed here, you have to be wily, enter prising and audacious. For the sake of his fortune, I would wish him half the talent and more than double his tact, and would not mind this."

Mozart's only two children to survive: Karl Thomas and Franz Zaver Wolfgang, who became music teachers.

On 27 July 1785, birth of Nannerl's son, Leopold, who will stay with his grandfather in Salzburg, who writes to his daughter and son-in-law.
I trust that you will have found [...] at 5 o'clock your husband and children, joyful and in good health. [...] To his son-in-law: I would beg you once more not to worry about the child - things should not be rushed: you have five children at home, the sixth is in good hands here [...] If you believe and wish that Leopold be returned to you, have confidence in me, I anticipate that one day he may be very safely returned [...]. But if my son wishes to leave Leopold with me in Salzburg, I would be very happy to take care of him and will give him back to you when he is nine months old. Nandl [the children's nanny] is still with me and I must say that she takes magnificent care of the child. It goes without saying that I will be happy to keep him at my expense.
26 July 1791, birth in Vienna of Mozart's sixth child, Franz Xaver Wolfgang, less than six months before the death of his father.

M	T	W	T	F	S	S
1	2	3	4	5	6	7
8	9	10	11	12	13	14
15	16	17	18	19	20	21
22	23	24	25	26	27	28
29	30	31				

JULY 31th **WEEK**

AUGUST

2 Friday
8

1 Thursday
8

9

31 Wednesday
8

9

10

30 Tuesday
8

9

10

11

29 Monday
8

9

10

11

12

9

10

11

12

13

10

11

12

13

14

11

12

13

14

15

12

13

14

15

16

13

14

15

16

17

14

15

16

17

18

15

16

17

18

19

16

17

18

19

20

17

18

19

20

1777 Salzburg. A high point of the summer for Wolfgang will be his meeting with the singer Josepha Duschek, coming from Prague, where they would meet again ten years later. Susceptible to her charms, Mozart writes the dramatic scene, *Andromeda*, for her.

18

19

20

1781 "The day before yesterday, young Stephanie gave me a libretto to compose *[Die Entführung aus dem Serail]*. I have to declare that even though he behaves spitefully towards other people, so much so that is difficult to imagine, he is a very good friend to me."

19

20

1783 Having postponing the journey so many times, Wolfgang and Constance arrive in Salzburg. The atmosphere will remain tense for the entire time they spend with Leopold.

20

1781 Gottlieb Stephanie, Inspector of the German Theatre in Vienna, writes the libretto for *Die Entführung aus dem Serail* for Mozart, this has to be performed on the occasion of the visit of Grand Duke Paul of Russia.

1791 Whilst he is working on the *The Magic Flute*, Mozart receives a mysterious commission for a requiem.

	4 Sunday
	8
3 Saturday	
	9
	10
0	11
1	12
2	13
3	14
4	15
5	16
6	17
7	18
8	19
9	20
0	

779 Salzburg. *Serenade N° 9 in D major*, called the *Posthorn Serenade*. Would the postillion's appeal be reminiscent of Mozart's escape from Colloredo ?

1782 Wolfgang marries Constance in Saint Stephen's Cathedral in Vienna. After paying the wedding taxes, Baroness von Waldstätten arranges a dinner for the newlyweds.

31 July 1751, birth in Salzburg of Maria Anna (called "Nanner"l). On 4 August 1782, Mozart marries Constance Weber in Vienna. Leopold's consent only arrives the day after. Wolf gang's letter dated 7 August.

I kiss your hands and thank you with all the affection that a son has ever felt towards his father, for the consent that you have been good enough to grant me and for your fatherly blessing. But I could fully count on it! - for you knew that I was only too well aware of all the objections that can always arise against such a move [...], so I could definitely count upon it ! This is the reason why, after waiting in vain for your answer to my two letters [...], I arranged the union before God with my beloved. The day after, I received your two letters together; now it is done ! - I would simply your forgiveness for my over-hasty confidence in your paternal love; in this sincere confession, you have further proof of my love for the truth and my horror of a lie. My dear wife will ask for a paternal blessing from her excellent father-in-law in her next letter, and will ask her beloved sister-in-law to extend to her in future her precious friendship.

Facing: Constance's portrait by Hans Hansen. Below: Saint Stephen's Cathedral in Vienna, where she married Wolfgang in 1782.

Mannheim
Under the sign of love

Located at the confluence of the Rhine and the Neckar, in the area near Heidelberg and Worms, further north, Mannheim had always been a strategic point on the broad trade route of the Rhine. Mannheim, a prosperous city, the jewel of the electoral principality of the Palatinate, had been ruined twice: devastated during the Thirty Year's War, then annihilated by the armies of Louis XIV during one of the most shameful wars in the history of France. It was then that Madame, Princess of the Palatinate, known as

Charles-Theodore, Prince of the Palatinate and Elector of Bavaria.

Liselotte, sister-in-law to the King of France, wept silently at Versailles, writing desesperate letters on the destiny of her country, while Louvois gave the orders to «burn and re-burn» the Palatinate. During this period, Mannheim was totally destroyed. «Louvois made his desert, but it cost us dearly in the esteem of the civilized world»: such would be the judgment of history. Nearly a century after these atrocious events, a young child with a very sprightly mind, already a musician, accompanied by his father and mother, as well as by his elder sister, travelled from east to west along the roads of Europe. Coming from the ecclesiastical principality of Salzburg, and travelling towards Paris, the family stopped at Mannheim, visited the Opera, the Princely Treasury, and the Library. Together, they went as far as Schwetzingen, the summer residence of the Prince Elector of the Palatinate, to hear an orchestra which the head of the family, Leopold, a master violinist, described as «without doubt the best in all Germany». It was summer; Wolfgang Mozart was seven years old; he had only passed through

Mannheim. Fifteen years later, accompanied only by his mother, he again roamed the roads of Germany, going from court to court, in search of a situation. The Palatinate formed a part of his ambitions. What riches awaited him in this city of Mannheim, which he had undoubtedly forgotten! The marvellous orchestra of forty-eight musicians playing like forty-eight soloists, with clarinettes, inexistent in Salzburg; the ready friendship of all these musician artists: Cannabich, *Konzertmeister* and composer; Ramm, oboist; Wendling, flautist; Franzl, violinist. Rediscovered with Kapellmeister Holzbauer, whom he had already met on his first trip through the city. Wolfgang participated in all the musical events of the city; in this way, he played about ten times, in the most official concerts as well as the most informal. Also illuminating this happy time of fraternal amity for the young man was the discovery of a marvelous soprano voice, that of a young girl with whom Mozart was immediately and madly taken, Aloysia Weber, whose servant-composer he intended to become, composing concert arias which were to be the best suited for putting the «cantabile» qualities of her soprano voice to best advantage. He spent five months at Mannheim, from

October 1777 to March 1778, but the hope of staying there dissipated little by little, while the plan of continuing on his way took shape, this time to Paris. He left the city with regret; he had been very happy there, but in the end he had failed. Mannheim had not offered him the position he hoped for. He had not even received a symphony commission for the most beautiful orchestra he had ever heard.
On his return from the disastrous trip to Paris, and against the will of his father, Wolgang insisted on not taking the usual route on the return trip to Salzburg, but chose the road passing through Mannheim. It would not be possible to see his beloved Aloysia, who had since moved to Munich, but he had other reasons for wanting to retrace his steps. He had just rediscovered an interest in melodrama, in the works of Benda *(Medea, Ariane at Naxos)*, and he made plans in this direction for himself, with Otto von Gemmingen as librettist, or with Count Dalberg, two personalities from Mannheim, a city he always dreamt of as center of the musical world. He had not yet understood that Mannheim would soon no longer be the same, since the Prince of the Palatinate, having become by inheritance the Elector of Bavaria, had moved to Munich

with his court. Wolfgang left Mannheim, where he remained only one short month (between November and December 1778). None of the plans which were born there ever materialized, yet at this time, the future of German opera became one of his central concerns.

Mozart passed through Mannheim on one last occasion. He joined in the coronation festivities of Emperor Leopold II at Frankfurt. He only stayed a few days, time to dash to Schwetzingen castle and hear *the Marriage of Figaro* in its first premiere in the Palatinate. The opera was sung there in German. It was the last gift Mannheim ever gave Mozart, who never returned to the Palatinate.

BRIGITTE MASSIN

Right, Count Dalberg, influential theatre intendant at Mannheim, who wished to make his city the center of a German cultural Renaissance, and who was to be the patron of Schiller. Below, the National Theatre of Mannheim, which had just been inaugurated when Mozart arrived at the court of Charles-Theodore.

M	T	W	T	F	S	S
			1	2	3	4
5	6	7	8	9	10	11
12	13	14	15	16	17	18
19	20	21	22	23	24	25
26	27	28	29	30	31	

AUGUST 32ⁿᵈ **WEEK**

9 Friday

8

8 Thursday

8

9

7 Wednesday

8

9

10

6 Tuesday

8

9

10

11

5 Monday

8

9

10

11

12

13

14

15

16

17

18

19

20

1782 Leopold's consent finally arrives, the day after the wedding of Wolfgang and Constance.

9

10

11

12

13

14

15

16

17

18

19

20

1782 Revival of *Die Entführung aus dem Serail* in Vienna, at the instigation of Gluck, who wishes to express his admiration to the composer by word of mouth.

9

10

11

12

13

14

15

16

17

18

19

20

1778 Mozart writes from Paris to Father Bullinger: "Salzburg is not the place for my talent ! Firstly, music circles are not given any considerations and secondly, you cannot listen to anything there: no theatre, no opera ! And if you really wanted to stage one, who would sing in it ?"

9

10

11

12

13

14

15

16

17

18

19

20

1781 Mozart who is working on the score for *Die Entführung aus dem Serail*, plays some of its passages to Countess Thun, whose support will be even more precious to him since she is a personal friend of Joseph II.

9

10

11

12

13

14

15

16

17

18

19

20

1791 Mozart has received a commission from Prague for a opera to celebrate the coronation of Leopold II as King of Bohemia. A libretto of Metastasio is imposed on him: *La Clemenza di Tito*.

11 Sunday

10 Saturday	
8	8
9	9
10	10
11	11
12	12
13	13
14	14
15	15
16	16
17	17
18	18
19	19
20	20

1787 Mozart completes in Vienna the *Serenade N° 13*, which will be christened *Eine kleine Nachtmusik*.

1770 In Bologna, Wolfgang and the son of Count Pallavicini form a friendship. "The young Count, who is the same age as Wolfgang and sole inheritor, has great talent. He plays the harpsichord, speaks German, Italian and French, and every day has five or six tutors in various subjects", writes Leopold. Wolfgang will share the lessons with his new friend and derive great benefit from them.

Neues Singspiel.

Die Kaiferl. Königl. National - Hof - Schaufpieler
werden heute Dienstag den 16 July 1782 aufführen:

(Zum erstenmal)

Die Entführung aus dem Serail.

Ein Singspiel in drey Aufzügen,
nach Bretzners frey bearbeitet und für das k. k. Nationalhoftheater eingerichtet.

In Musik gesetzt vom Herrn Kapellmeister Mozart

Die Bücher find beym Logenmeister für 17. kr. zu haben.

Der Anfang ist um halb 7 Uhr.

Above, poster for "Die Entführung aus dem Serail" for the 1782 revival. At the top is the word "Singspiel". Mozart's work was written in fact within the framework of the German style comic opera, but adopted the style somewhat inconsistently.
Right, Gluck, who so much appreciated this opera that he invited the composer and his wife to lunch.

7 August 1781, Mozart plays some passages from his new opera, "Die Entführung aus dem Serail" (K 384) to Countess Maria Wilhemina Thun, a friend of the arts, whose patronage will never desert him. She gives a very favourable opinion, evidenced by the letter written the day after to Leopold.

Adamberger, La Cavalieri and Fischer [who perform the roles of Belmonte, Constance and Osmin] are extremely satisfied with their arias. Yesterday, I lunched with Countess Thun and am also invited there again tomorrow. - I let her hear all that is completed. She told me at the end that she would pledge her life that what I have written so far would definitely delight. - But as for this, I am not taking any notice of *the praise or criticism of anyone* before the public has heard and seen it all - I would rather trust my own feelings. All the same you may see in all this how much it must have satisfied her.

6 August 1782, revival of "Die Entführung aus dem Serail" at the request of Gluck who appreciates the work so much that he invites the composer and his young wife to lunch. Mozart's letter to his father dated 7 August 1782.

My opera was restaged yesterday (at Gluck's request); Gluck paid me many *compliments*. I am lunching with him tomorrow.

M	T	W	T	F	S	S
			1	2	3	4
5	6	7	8	9	10	11
12	13	14	15	16	17	18
19	20	21	22	23	24	25
26	27	28	29	30	31	

AUGUST 33rd WEEK

12 Monday

8
9
10
11
12
13
14
15
16
17
18
19
20

1773 Maria Theresa grants an audience to Wolfgang and Leopold to whom she is predisposed.

13 Tuesday

8
9
10
11
12
13
14
15
16
17
18
19
20

1771 Still accompanied by Leopold, Wolfgang leaves again for Milan after a short stop in Salzburg.

14 Wednesday

8
9
10
11
12
13
14
15
16
17
18
19
20

1790 Vienna. Mozart sends an SOS to Puchberg. He has never been in a worse situation.

15 Thursday

8
9
10
11
12
13
14
15
16
17
18
19
20

1772 Salzburg. Colloredo designates Mozart to the post of *Konzertmeiser* but prefers Fischietti to him as Choirmaster.

16 Friday

8
9
10
11
12
13
14
15
16
17
18
19
20

1789 Restored to health, Constance finds quartiers in Baden for the summer. Her frivolity worries her husband: "I am delighted when you are happy - of course ! But I would only wish that you would be more reserved than you have been up to now... You may rest assured that only good behaviour from a wife can please her husband."

18 Sunday

17 Saturday

8

9

10

11

12

13

14

15

16

17

18

19

20

1791 Accompanied by his disciple Süssmayr and the clarinetist Stadler, Mozart leaves for Prague. At the very moment that he is preparing to enter the carriage, a messenger comes to him to ask for news of the *Requiem*.

1782 Vienna still does not recognise the value of Mozart who, in spite of his successes, thinks of returning to London or Paris.

"The Former Fishing Quarter in Lyon", by Michel Grobon. In 1766, the Mozarts, who had left Salzburg in 1763, were on their way back home. From Paris, they took the road to Dijon, where they gave a concert, then Lyon, where they also performed, before making their way to Geneva.

14 August 7166, the Mozart children give a concert in Lyon. Johann Rudolf Forcart was present. The following day, he writest o his brother-in-law Isaac Iselin in Basle to give him his impressions.

My dear brother-in-Law

Here we have Mr Mozart, Choirmaster to the Prince of Salzburg, who is travelling around Europe with his son and daughter who are prodigies on the Harpsichord; you may perhaps recall having read about him in the Basle gazette some years ago at the time he was in Paris; the son is 9 years old and the daughter 14. They gave a concert here a few days ago, when they played the most difficult things and all the Symphonies played were the Composition of this small *virtuosus*, and he played a pre lude for a quarter of an hour with the most skilful masters around here and was their equal. Finally, you have to see it to believe it, such is the wording on the poster, and myself and everybody else were delighted. There were more than 300 Persons at this Concert at 3 francs per Person, for it is said that on this day he earned close to 1,000 francs. If by chance he wants to go to Basle, he will not earn as much from it, although proportionally there are more people who can afford to spend plenty of Money than here.

M	T	W	T	F	S	S
			1	2	3	4
5	6	7	8	9	10	11
12	13	14	15	16	17	18
19	20	21	22	23	24	25
26	27	28	29	30	31	

AUGUST   34th WEEK

23 Friday
8
9
10
11
12
13
14
15
16
17
18
19
20

1773 After an escape in Baden, Leopold and Wolfgang return to Vienna.

22 Thursday
8
9
10
11
12
13
14
15
16
17
18
19
20

1781 Mozart completes the first act of *Die Entführung aus dem Serail* in Vienna.

21 Wednesday
8
9
10
11
12
13
14
15
16
17
18
19
20

1778 Leopold writes to Father Martini for the tenor Raaf to get a letter of introduction from him to Charles Theodore, who is henceforth installed in Munich after inheriting the Electorate of Bavaria. In Paris, Wolfgang is abandoned by Grimm whom he considered his patron.

20 Tuesday
8
9
10
11
12
13
14
15
16
17
18
19
20

1791 On the way to Prague, Mozart works without respite on *La Clemenza di Tito*. He will fall ill just as he arrives.

19 Monday
8
9
10
11
12
13
14
15
16
17
18
19
20

1783 Whilst in Strasbourg, Wolfgang and Constance learn of the death of Raymond their first child.

24 Saturday

8

9

10

11

12

13

14

15

16

17

18

19

20

1787 Vienna. *Sonata for violin and piano in A major* K 526.

25 Sunday

8

9

10

11

12

13

14

15

16

17

18

19

20

1786 First performance in Salzburg of the *Solemn Mass for the Acts of Grace:* Wolfgang fulfils the promise made in July 1782 during Constance's illness, but like all the works inspired by his wife, this mass remains unfinished and he will have to borrow from previous works.

Nannerl in 1785 (anonymous portrait), one year after her marriage to Baron Johann Baptist von Berchtold zu Sonnenburg, Counsellor to the Court of Salzburg.

23 August 1784, Nannerl marries Baron von Sonnerburg. On 18 August, her brother sent her a letter and a poem for the occasion.

Good Heavens! it is time to write now if I want my letter to find you still a vertale virgin! - a few days later and - that would be that. [...] So please accept a bit of advice drawn from the little poetry cupboard in my brain:

"So if your husband gives you the cold shoulder
"When you think you do not deserve it
"If he is at all spiteful to you
"Think: It is just one of the vagaries of men
"And say: Sire, let your will be done
"In the day - and mine at night."

Your sincere brother, W. A. Mozart

M	T	W	T	F	S	S
			1	2	3	4
5	6	7	8	9	10	11
12	13	14	15	16	17	18
19	20	21	22	23	24	25
26	27	28	29	30	31	

AUGUST — 35th WEEK

26 Monday
8
9
10
11
12
13
14
15
16
17
18
19
20

1763 The third concert by the Mozart children in Frankfurt, where they arrived on 12 August.

27 Tuesday
8
9
10
11
12
13
14
15
16
17
18
19
20

1778 Wolfgang is pleased to meet his friend Johan Christian Bach again in Paris. He accompanies him for a few days to Saint Germain to the home of the Count of Noailles.

28 Wednesday
8
9
10
11
12
13
14
15
16
17
18
19
20

1777 Finally, in reply to Leopold's letters requesting a leave of absence for him and his son and a subsequent offer to resign, Colloredo grants them "permission to go and seek their fortune elsewhere". A few days later, Leopold learns that he can keep his position, but Wolfgang is dismissed.

29 Thursday
8
9
10
11
12
13
14
15
16
17
18
19
20

1781 Vienna. Yielding to entreaties from a Leopold worried and unhappy because of the gossip reaching him, Wolfgang leaves the Weber home to settle a couple of steps away.

30 Friday
8
9
10
11
12
13
14
15
16
17
18
19
20

1763 Fourth and last concert of the Mozart children in Frankfurt, for which Leopold had a notice inserted in the local press, in which he evokes "the admiration which is awakened in the souls of the whole audience by the skilfulness - never yet seen nor heard at such a level - of the two children of the choirmaster." Goethe, then aged 14 years, was present at one of these concerts and heard Mozart. In 1830, he still remembered perfectly "this little man with his wig and his sword".

SEPTEMBER

1 Sunday

31 Saturday

8

9

10

11

12

13

14

15

16

17

18

19

20

1778 Salzburg. Because of his scheming, Leopold obtains the post of organist for Wolfgang. There will be no question of that of Choirmaster, made vacant by the disappearance of Lolli.

1783 As a token of his admiration and friendship, Mozart dedicates the six quartets completed in January to Haydn. The music lovers for their part will be confused by the originality of this series.

29 August 1789, revival of "The Marriage of Figaro" (K 492) in Vienna where the opera had received a rather lukewarm reception during its first performance on 1 May 1786. This time the Viennese proved quite enthusiastic, as though they had waited for the ovation given to Mozart in Prague (for the same "Marriage" and for "Don Giovanni") to break through their reserve. Some time before, Mozart was writing to his wife who was taking the waters in Baden.

My darling little wife!

I was happy to read your dear letter - and hope that you will have received my second with the infusion, the honey medicine and the ants eggs. At 5 o'clock tomorrow morning, I am hoisting the sail - if only it were for the simple pleasure of seeing you again and taking you into my arms, I would not leave again so soon, but they are soon going to restage my *Figaro* to which I have to make a few changes which makes my presence necessary at the rehearsals. - So I will have to return for the 19th - but to stay her until the 19th without you would be impossible. *On 31 August of the same year, Count Zinzendorf mentions this revival of "The Marriage" in Vienna in his diary.* At the opera, *The Marriage of Figaro.* Delightful duet between La Cavalieri et la Ferraresi.

The stage-set for "the Marriage of Figaro", during a revival at the Fenice in Venice. The opera achieved incredible popularity in Prague, which welcomed Mozart as a conquering hero.

Paris 1778
Sad Return of the Prodigal Son

When the decision was made to leave Salzburg and look elsewhere for the unfound resources with which to compose, to have his operas performed, and above all to write an opera, Mozart set off on a journey which was to take him to Paris. The European capital of music offered him —a priori— everything he hoped for. The flutist Wendling, in fact, described it to him this way: «It is the only place where one can make money and achieve honours… all you need do is write operas— serious, comic, oratory, everything. Anyone who writes operas in Paris earns a dependable income every year. And then, there is the Concert Spirituel, the academie des amateurs, where you get five gold louis for a symphony. If you give lessons, it is usual for you to earn three gold louis for twelve lessons. Then your sonatas, trios and quartets are engraved for public subscription» (1). This was just what Mozart was dreaming of: «Nothing gladdens me more than the Concert Spirituel» (2), or, again, «The idea of writing an opera never leaves me», he wrote at

Mannheim (3). In Paris, moreover, this was accompanied by the possibility of earning a decent living and having his works edited. Mozart set off for the city of music. The city where opera is a subject of such importance that it is likely to eclipse great political problems and awaken the most ardent disputes and debates. All the more so where philosophers and men of letters, since the middle of the century, had conferred upon the art of music the status of an entirely independent subject of analysis. His sejours in Paris might have been a privilieged meeting point

between vivid and rich musical reflection, and a musical creation which was turning the course of musical history towards new concepts. It is not hard to imagine what Mozart might have found or accomplished in Paris. But instead, failure. Leopold, upon their departure from Salzburg, had stimulated his son with the phrase «Aut Caesar, aut nihil». A few months later, the exhortation would seem ludicrous in view of the alarming reality. Mozart met nothing but indifference in Paris, the polite, mundane reserve and condescending flattery. The city of hope melted away beneath his tread. Plans evaporated, doors barely half-open closed again,

concerned» (4). It marked a decisive turning point in Mozartian creation. From this city, which received him so poorly, Mozart was able to derive richness. If the Parisians closed their ears to his music, he knew how to open his ears to their own; and that, no one could prevent him from doing.

MARIE-CHRISTINE VILA

1) Letter from Mozart to Leopold. Mannheim, 3 December 1777.
(2) Letter from Mozart to Leopold. Mannheim, 28 December 1778.
(3) Post-script by Mozart to letter from Anna Maria to Leopold, Mannheim, 7 February 1778.
(4) Letter from Mozart to Leopold. Paris, 11 September 1778.

without a sound. And that was the worst thing. This repulse was not occasioned by any scandal. Indifference was doing its work in silence. Nevertheless, the scandal existed. It lay in an obvious, increasing deafness towards the musician. In a city adulating discussion, where, moreover, discussion constitutes a major wealth of that city, Mozart's music was drowned in a babble of nonsense, of radical position taking, of flattery and sycophancy, which substituted for thought and discussion. Music was so much talked about that people forgot to listen. He who had no weapons with which to fight except notes on a staff,

melodies instruments, and voice, went unnoticed. Paris received a peerless musician and was not even aware of it. Or perhaps too much talent disturbed them, interfering with the droning of pre-digested ideas which fed the dispute of the moment over Gluck's opera style. What could they do with a young German who refused to be classified under a label —lyric tragedy, Italian opera, Gluck or Piccinni? Ignore him. Mozart's hopes were dashed on the streets of Paris. Nevertheless, his failure should not obscure the importance of his stay, of which Mozart remarked, «I assure you that this trip has not been unserviceable for me— as far as composition is

Above, "Walking in the garden of the Royal Palace" (engraving by Debucourt). Left, Nicco Piccinni (1728-1800). Opposite, manuscript of the "Paris Symphony" in D major, KV 297.

M	T	W	T	F	S	S
						1
2	3	4	5	6	7	8
9	10	11	12	13	14	15
16	17	18	19	20	21	22
23	24	25	26	27	28	29
30						

SEPTEMBER 36th WEEK

6 Friday

8

9

10

11

12

13

14

15

16

17

18

19

20

1791 The evening of the coronation of Leopold II as King of Bohemia, the curtain rises in Prague on *La Clemenza di Tito*. The work, written in eighteen days, displeases the Empress who, detesting these new subjects, calls the production a *porcheria tedesca*.

5 Thursday

8

9

10

11

12

13

14

15

16

17

18

19

20

1781 After leaving the Weber's home, Wolfgang tries to justify himself with Leopold, reproaching him for his lack of confidence: "Unfortunately I note - as though I were a good-for-nothing or an idiot our both at the same time - that you believe more of what others say or write than in me.

4 Wednesday

8

9

10

11

12

13

14

15

16

17

18

19

20

1776 An absolutely conscience-stricken Mozart writes to Father Martin to ask advice. For every instance, he encloses a hur riedly composed motet in his letter..

3 Tuesday

8

9

10

11

12

13

14

15

16

17

18

19

20

1778 "You do not like Paris" , writes Leopold to Wolfgang. And to encourage his son to return to Salzburg, he promises that he will be able to correspond freely with Aloysia.

2 Monday

8

9

10

11

12

13

14

15

16

17

18

19

20

1787 Mozart leaves for Prague with Constance and Da Ponte to work there on his *Don Giovanni*.

7 Saturday

8

9

10

11

12

13

14

15

16

17

18

19

20

1771 Leopold writes from Milan to his wife who is still in Salzburg: "The heavens have at last refreshed us with a little shower several days running... Now we are up to our ears with other problems for the libretto [for Ascanio in Alba] did not arrive until very late. The poet [Parini] kept it until the day before yesterday to make this or that change to it.

8 Sunday

8

9

10

11

12

13

14

15

16

17

18

19

20

1778 The second Paris Symphony is performed at the Spiritual Concert.

Above, Mozart's letter to Haydn (on the medallion on the right), mentioned below. It will be noted that it is written in Italian. Mozart's letters often provide a savoury mixture of different languages.

1 September 1785, Mozart dedicates his Six Quartets (K 387, 421, 428, 458, 464 and 465) to Joseph Haydn, who has always shown him much kindness and whom he respectfully and affection ately called "Papa".

My dear friend Haydn, A father determined to send his sons around the big wide world feels he ought to entrust them into the protection and guidance of a man though famous who, happily, was in addition his best friend. Accordingly, I am turning my six sons over to you, a famous man and my very dear friend. It is true they are the fruit of long and laborious efforts, but the hope given to me by the many friends who have seen them partly recompenses, encourages me and I flatter myself to think that one day they will be of some consolation to me. You, my dear friend, during your last stay in this capital expressed your satisfaction with them. It is your vote of approval especially that prompts me to recommend them to you and leaves me to hope that they will not seem too unworthy of your favour. Be kind enough to welcome them fondly and be their father, guide and friend ! From now on, I am giving up my rights in them; I would beg you to look indulgently upon the faults that the biased eye of a father could have hidden from me, and to uphold, in spite of them, your generous friendship to the one who appreciates it and whole-heartedly remains your very dear friend,

Your most sincere friend,
W. A. Mozart

M	T	W	T	F	S	S
						1
2	3	4	5	6	7	8
9	10	11	12	13	14	15
16	17	18	19	20	21	22
23	24	25	26	27	28	29
30						

SEPTEMBER   37th WEEK

9 Monday

8
9
10
11
12
13
14
15
16
17
18
19
20

1790 Mozart is not invited to the coronation festivities in Frankfurt. He decides to get there under his own steam.

10 Tuesday

8
9
10
11
12
13
14
15
16
17
18
19
20

1791 Prague. Mozart is sad to leave his friends in Bohemia and reaches Vienna, more tired than ever.

11 Wednesday

8
9
10
11
12
13
14
15
16
17
18
19
20

1767 The Mozarts leave Salzburg yet again for Vienna, where the wedding of the Archduchess Maria Joseph to the King of Naples was to take place, but an epidemic of smallpox carries off the fiancee. All the festivities planned will be cancelled.

12 Thursday

8
9
10
11
12
13
14
15
16
17
18
19
20

1775 Salzburg. *Third Concerto for violin.*

13 Friday

8
9
10
11
12
13
14
15
16
17
18
19
20

1771 Milan. A few months after his first flirtation with his sister's young friend, Wolfgang regresses: "Tell Mlle von Mölk that I am overjoyed to come back to Salzburg so that I can once more receive a present for the minuets similar to the one I received at her Academy: she already knows this."

14 Saturday

8
9
10
11
12
13
14
15
16
17
18
19
20

15 Sunday

8
9
10
11
12
13
14
15
16
17
18
19
20

1768 There is a frenzied plot in Vienna to prevent the first performance of *La finta semplice*. Leopold is embittered but determined to fight: "As for Wolfgang's opera, I can only tell you one thing: that all the devils in music are unleashed to prevent the talent of a child from being recognised." He will however have to give up performing the work in Vienna, and the first performance will not take place until 1 May 1769 in Salzburg.

1773 "The death of Doctor Niederl [a family friend] has greatly affected us. We can tell you we have copiously cried, snivelled, howled and wept. Our compliments to all the good souls who praise the Lord God", writes Wolfgang to his sister, from Vienna.

A street scene i n Amsterdam (picture by Isaak Ouwater). In 1765, the Mozarts are in Holland where Nannerl falls seriously ill.

9 September 1765, The Mozart family arrives in Rotterdam, then travels on to The Hague. On 19 September, Leopold Mozart gives his impressions to his friend in Salzburg, Johann Lorenz Hage nauer.

We only stayed half a day in Rotterdam. We left in the afternoon by trek-schuit [boat] for The Hague, which we had already reached at 7 o'clock. Now I must say that I would have been sorry not to have seen Holland: if all the cities in Europe I have seen had one or the other similarity, in Holland the villages as well as the towns are totally different from the rest of Europe. This would take too long to explain, but suffice it to say that their cleanliness (which may seem excessive to some of our number) pleased me a lot, and I only want you to note that I was pleased to admire the statue of the renowned Erasmus on the square in Rotterdam. We have now spent a week in The Hague and have already been twice to visit the Princess and once to see the Prince of Orange [William V], who arranged for us to be taken and brought back home with his carriage and horses; but my daughter was not with us, since it is now her turn, and she has bad bronchitus from which she is only starting to get better. As soon as she is well, we will go back and visit the Prince of Orange and the Princess of Weilburg as well as the Count of Wolfenbüttel. The journey has been paid for, but I have to see who will pay for the return, as I would not like to touch my money from Amsterdam.

M	T	W	T	F	S	S
						1
2	3	4	5	6	7	8
9	10	11	12	13	14	15
16	17	18	19	20	21	22
23	24	25	26	27	28	29
30						

SEPTEMBER 38th WEEK

16 Monday

8

9

10

11

12

13

14

15

16

17

18

19

20

1763 Mainz. The Mozarts are preparing to leave for Koblenz, from where they will go down the Rhine as far as Bonn.

17 Tuesday

8

9

10

11

12

13

14

15

16

17

18

19

20

1773 Before leaving Vienna, Mozart receives the commission for *Thamos re d'Egitto*, an "heroic" , German drama (from a play by Baron Gebler) which makes reference to the mysteries of Freemasonry.

18 Wednesday

8

9

10

11

12

13

14

15

16

17

18

19

1762 The Mozart family takes the road to Vienna. The first long journey for Nannerl and Wolfgang. They will arrive on 6 October.

19 Thursday

8

9

10

11

12

13

14

15

16

17

18

19

20

1781 Wolfgang to Nannerl: "I want to write to you in sincerity, precisely on the question of your continual indispositions. Believe me, my darling sister, the best cure would be to find yourself a husband".

20 Friday

8

9

10

11

12

13

14

15

16

17

18

19

20

1768 As Affligio, Director of the Viennese Theatre, refuses to stage *La finta semplice*, Leopold writes out a *Species facti*, a letter of complaint that he will hand over to the Emperor during the following day's audience.

22 Sunday

21 Saturday

8	8
9	9
10	10
11	11
12	12
13	13
14	14
15	15
16	16
17	17
18	18
19	19
20	20

1784 Birth in Vienna of Karl Thomas Mozart. After losing little Raymund at an early age, Wolfgang and Constance will be happier with this second child. They move home on this event.

1790 In spite of everything, Mozart is resolved to visit Frankfurt, but has to obtain the money needed for the journey. Hence he pawns the few possessions of value he possesses with Lackenbacher the usurer. Departure is arranged for the day after.

18 September 1762, the entire Mozart family undertakes its first trip to Vienna. Leopold Mozart does not hide his satisfaction to Johann Lorenz Hagenauer. From Linz, 3 September 1762.

Moreover, my children are astonished with everything they see, especially my son. Count *Herberstein* has left for Vienna and is going to announce us with a great deal of fuss. And yesterday, *Count von Schlick,* who is the administrative head of the province, left for Vienna with his wife. Both of them have been extremely pleasant to us; they have said that we shall have to visit them as soon as we arrive in Vienna; that in the meantime they will speak to Count Durazzo [the then Theatrical Director] and will announce our coming everywhere in Vienna.

Thus it seems that the undertaking has to go quite well. Let God protect us as he has up to now, we are all well. I feel some slight twinges of gout here and there. The children are gay and feel at home anywhere. My son gets on well with everybody, especially with officials, as though he has always known them.

View of Vienna at the time Leopold arrived with his children to seek his fortune.

M	T	W	T	F	S	S
						1
2	3	4	5	6	7	8
9	10	11	12	13	14	15
16	17	18	19	20	21	22
23	24	25	26	27	28	29
30						

SEPTEMBER — 39th WEEK

23 Monday

8
9
10
11
12
13
14
15
16
17
18
19
20

1777 Wolfgang leaves Salzburg, after obtaining his freedom, whilst his father is compelled to stay at court.

24 Tuesday

8
9
10
11
12
13
14
15
16
17
18
19
20

1778 "Keep your medicines in your overnight bag. Pay attention to your luggage getting in and out of carriages. Do not show your money to anyone", writes Leopold to his 22-year-old globe-trotting son.

25 Wednesday

8
9
10
11
12
13
14
15
16
17
18
19
20

1777 Salzburg. Leopold has a very heavy heart after the departure of his wife and son: I climbed upstairs and threw myself into a chair. I had done my all at the moment of separation not to make our goodbyes even more painful... Nannerl was crying as hard as she could... A very distressed dog Pimperl, stayed close to her.

26 Thursday

8
9
10
11
12
13
14
15
16
17
18
19
20

1766 Wolfgang has to resolve to leave Paris for Salzburg, urged by Grimm, who, in connivance with Leopold, puts him in a coach bound for the border, a little like getting rid of a cumbersome package.

27 Friday

8
9
10
11
12
13
14
15
16
17
18
19
20

1788 To show his gratitude to Puchberg, who has kindly agreed him loans, Mozart, after the *Trios* K 542 and 548 offers him his *Divertimento* K 563.

28 Saturday

8

9

10

11

12

13

14

15

16

17

18

19

20

1771 First rehearsals in Milan of *Ascanio in Alba*, which Wolfgang wrote in three weeks.

29 Sunday

8

9

10

11

12

13

14

15

16

17

18

19

20

1791 First night of *The Magic Flute* at the Auf der Wieden Theatre. Mozart conducts from the harpsichord. Disconcerted at first by the first act, the public allows itself to be conquered by the work which brings the roof down every night.

"Voltaire at Ferney", by Huber. The travellers who made a detour on the Swiss side of the border in the hope of meeting the famous philosopher were numerous. Leopold was no exception but his wait was a disappointment.

On their way back from England, the Mozarts stopped in Paris, then left the French capital in July 1766. Each stage is the pretext for a concert or a visit to local dignitaries. Leopold arrives in Geneva in the autumn and would like to introduce his children to Voltaire. But the philosopher from Ferney in reality hardly proved accessible, although he had written to Madame d'Épinay.
Ferney, 26 September 1766.
[...] Your little Mazar [sic], dear lady, has, I believe, chosen his time rather badly to bring harmony into the Temple of Discord. You know that I live eight kilometres from Geneva: I never go out; I was very ill when this phenomenal star shone on the black horizon at Geneva. Finally, he has left, to my great regret, without my having seen him. I have been transplanted and am having comic operas performed in my little theatre in Ferney for my convalescence; the whole company from Geneva, numbering fifty, was kind enough to do this to for my pleasure.

M	T	W	T	F	S	S
						1
2	3	4	5	6	7	8
9	10	11	12	13	14	15
16	17	18	19	20	21	22
23	24	25	26	27	28	29
30						

SEPTEMBER 40th WEEK

OCTOBER

30 Monday
8
9
10
11
12
13
14
15
16
17
18
19
20

1765 Nannerl is smitten by pneumonia. Wolfgang gives the concert on his own.

1 Tuesday
8
9
10
11
12
13
14
15
16
17
18
19
20

1768 Vienna. First performance of *Bastien und Bastienne* in the rural theatre of Doctor Mesmer, whose work on animal magnetism will soon earn him international fame.

2 Wednesday
8
9
10
11
12
13
14
15
16
17
18
19
20

1782 Vienna. Baroness von Waldstätten is the first to be notified of Constance's pregnancy.

3 Thursday
8
9
10
11
12
13
14
15
16
17
18
19
20

1790 The journey to Frankfurt is a total failure. Mozart, whose increasing distaste for society causes him to live as a recluse, has only one commission for which to put pen to paper: *Adagio for a mechanical organ.*

4 Friday
8
9
10
11
12
13
14
15
16
17
18
19
20

1763 The Mozart family arrives in Brussels, last long scheduled stop before Paris, which Leopold does not want to reach before the season is in full swing.

9

10

11

12

13

14

15

16

17

18

19

20

0

1

2

3

4

5

6

7

8

9

0

1781 Vienna. Composition on *Die Entführung aus dem Serail* is making no progress. Mozart asks Gottlieb Stephanie to make changes to his libretto.

1791 Mozart recovers some of his zest for life following the success of *The Magic Flute* in Vienna.

30 September 1791, first performance of "The Magic Flute" at the Auf der Wieden Theatre. Mozart joyfully informs his dear Constance of this success on 7-8 October; her failing health causes her to stay in Baden.

I am starting straightaway with the opera - it was full, as always. *The Mann und Wieb* duet etc. and the *Glockenspiel* from the first act had to be given an encore, as usual - just like the trio of young boys from the second act. But what gives me pleasure, is the *silent success* ! Then you may notice how much this opera is becoming appreciated more and more. Now this is what I have been doing: immediately after your departure, I played two games of billiards with Mr von Mozart (the one who wrote for Schikaneder); then I sold my horse for 14 ducats; after that I asked Joseph to call Primus to bring me some black coffee that I drank whilst smoking a pipe of marvellous tobacco; then I did the instrumentation for nearly all the Stadler *Rondo* [third movement of K 622].

[...] The most astonishing thing about all this, is that the evening that my new opera had so much success at its first performance, on the same evening in Prague, *Titus* was performed for the last time, also extraordinarily successfully. All the numbers were applauded. : Bedini [famous eunuch, with the rôle of Sesto], the small duet in A by the two young girls [N°.7] gave an encore, and - if they had not wanted to spare Marchetti [woman singer who took the Vitellia rôle] - they would have wanted to repeat the Rondo [N°. 23]. Stadler obtained (Oh what a Bohemian miracle ! he writes) bravos from the house and even from the orchestra.

Stage-set for the second act of "The Magic Flute", created by Joseph and Peter Schaffer for a revival of the opera in Vienna, in 1793.

Prague
A Bohemian Life

There are very few things of which Prague is so proud, and justly so, as having loved Mozart and having offered him the most glorious triumphs of his life. While *the Marriage of Figaro* had only nine performances in Vienna in 1786, it enchanted Prague, where it held the bill all winter, and a request from the musicians in the orchestra invited Mozart to come in person to conduct them. An entire month was filled with nothing but festivities for the composer: delirious enthusiasm at the theatre; balls where «all the people, so cordially joyous, threw themselves into gyrations to the tunes from my *Figaro*, arranged in the style of good German quadrilles», concerts where Mozart, « beaming with hapiness», improvised on *Non piu andrai* and set the elated Bohemians» ablaze.

Thus Mozart departed, in February 1787, with an order for an opera, *Don Giovanni*, which he began in Vienna and finally finished in Prague in September. The memories evoked by the Czechs with such veneration date from this period: the house «with the three golden lions» (Uhelny thr no.1), where he lodged across the street from Da Ponte, and they were able to converse from their windows; the small public houses where he drank punch while discussing the part of Leporello with Casanova and Da Ponte; the Strahov convent, where he come to play the organ; the beautiful baroque palace belonging to Count Thun, a fellow Mason, with its hanging garden above the old quarter of Mala Strana and of the Vltava. And above all, the charming Villa Bertamka, belonging to his friends Frantisek and Josefa Duschek in the hollow of a steep-sloped wooded dale, where Mozart finished his opera, writing the overture in one night while Constance read him fairy tales, if we are to believe the legend. Here, more than anywhere else, (with the exception of his house in Salzburg) is where we rediscover Mozart, in the midst of his souvenirs, portraits, manuscripts, posters, newspaper articles, sweet meat boxes, cuff links, music boxes, piano, white harpsichord, and violins, and the room with interlaced beams, painted with branches and multicoloured flowers, where he slept…

But we are hardly less moved upon entering the Tyl theatre, completely gilded, with pews for thirteen hundred people and its classical façade, where,

Above, view of Prague with the Charles Bridge and its statues of saints. Mozart received an unforgettable welcome here when he came to conduct the "Marriage of Figaro". There were also faithful friends, such as the Count Thun and the singer Josefa Duschek, who generously made her house available to him while he worked on the score of "Don Giovanni" (left), after the departure of Lorenzo da Ponte (right). Nevertheless he did not accept the offers made to him to remain in Prague, saying that he could not remain away from Vienna —he who was to try so long, and in vain, to obtain a position in foreign courts.

on 29 October 1787, *Don Giovanni* was frantically applauded. It would be performed regularly in Italian for fifteen years and then, in the German translation, one hundred sixteen times between 1796 and 1825! In August 1791, Mozart returned to Prague; in the act of getting into a coach in Vienna, «the man in black» approached to enquire about his *Requiem*. In the jerky coach he worked feverishly on la *Clemenza di Tito*, which he had agreed to write for Leopold's coronation at Prague. Suffering from illness, he met, happily his friends Duschek and Bertramka.

In eighteen hours of forced labour, he finished this marvellous work. But the premiere was a failure. Mozart did not hold a grudge against the Prague which so loved him. He parted with a broken heart, and on passing through the city gates, broke into tears. Several months later, four thousand people attended the first Requiem Mass sung in Mozart's memory; the soprano in Rössler's *Requiem* was Josefa Duschek, for whom Mozart had written, upon his departure from Prague in 1787, *Bella mia fiamma addio!* (12 May 1967)

JACQUES LONCHAMPT

M	T	W	T	F	S	S
	1	2	3	4	5	6
7	8	9	10	11	12	13
14	15	16	17	18	19	20
21	22	23	24	25	26	27
28	29	30	31			

OCTOBER 41ᵗʰ WEEK

7 Monday

8
9
10
11
12
13
14
15
16
17
18
19
20

1791 Vienna. Mozart completes the *Concerto for clarinet* commissioned from him by Stadler.

8 Tuesday

8
9
10
11
12
13
14
15
16
17
18
19
20

1780 The Salzburg theatre is hired out to the company of Schikaneder. Wolfgang assiduously attends the performances, one a ballet, *The Life like Statues*: is his first encounter with the theme of Don Juan.

9 Wednesday

8
9
10
11
12
13
14
15
16
17
18
19
20

1770 Wolfgang is accepted as a member of the Philharmonic Academy of Bologna and is congratulated by the examiners.

10 Thursday

8
9
10
11
12
13
14
15
16
17
18
19
20

1773 On his return to Salzburg, Wolfgang is smitten with a creative fever to last until the first weeks of 1774. He completes *Thamos re d'Egitto*, writes his first string quartet, first concerto for piano and three symphonies.

11 Friday

8
9
10
11
12
13
14
15
16
17
18
19
20

1777 Still accompanied by his mother, Wolfgang leaves Munich for Augsburg, for all attempts to obtain a post at the Bavarian Court have been fruitless, in spite of all the esteem felt for him by Prince Elector Charles Theodore, who had been literally enchanted by *La finta giardiniera* three years earlier.

8

9

10

11

12

13

14

15

16

17

18

19

20

1762 Arriving in Vienna on 6 October, the Mozarts receive an audience with Maria Theresa.

1777 Only just arrived in Augsburg, where he lodges with an uncle, Wolfgang makes the acquaintance of Stein, the famous piano-maker. Throughout the entire visit, great complicity binds him to his cousin, the malicious Maria Thekla, who initiates him into not very innocent games.

Maria Theresa of Austria, She let herself be charmed and moved by the infant prodigy.

13 October 1762, the Mozarts are received at Schönbrunn by Empress Maria Theresa, who wants to meet the two famous child prodigies. Letter from Leopold to his friend Hagenauer, 11-16 October 1762.

They are already talking about us almost everywhere and when on the 10th instant, I went alone to the opera, I heard Archduke Leopold tell someone who was sitting in a box next to his, amongst other things, that a small boy was in Vienna who played the piano so well, etc., etc. At 11 o'clock the same evening, I received the order to visit Schönbrunn on the 12th. I have only just time to hurriedly add that we have been welcomed by Their Majesties with such extraordinary kindness that if I were to talk about it, you would think I was making it up. [...] Wollferl jumped into the lap of the Empress, put his arms around her neck and gave her kisses like he does. In short, we were with her from 3 to 6 o'clock, and the Emperor [Francis of Lorraine] drove me himself so he could hear the child play the violin.

M	T	W	T	F	S	S
	1	2	3	4	5	6
7	8	9	10	11	12	13
14	15	16	17	18	19	20
21	22	23	24	25	26	27
28	29	30	31			

OCTOBER 42th WEEK

18 Friday
8
9
10
11
12
13
14
15
16
17
18
19
20

1791 Mozart and Constance have returned home from Baden. Concerned for the health of her husband, the young woman tries to distract him.

17 Thursday
8
9
10
11
12
13
14
15
16
17
18
19
20

1771 First performance in Milan of *Ascanio in Alba* and a fresh triumph for Wolfgang.

16 Wednesday
8
9
10
11
12
13
14
15
16
17
18
19
20

1786 Birth in Vienna of the third child of Wolfgang and Constance, Johann Thomas, whose godfather will be the editor Trattner.

15 Tuesday
8
9
10
11
12
13
14
15
16
17
18
19
20

1778 Coming from Paris, Wolfgang stops in Strasbourg. He then learns that Aloysia has been engaged by the Munich Opera. The return to Salzburg is nothing but bitter.

14 Monday
8
9
10
11
12
13
14
15
16
17
18
19
20

1787 Prague. First planned for today, 14 October, the first night of *Don Giovanni* has to be postponed until the 29th.

8

9

10

11

12

13

14

15

16

17

18

19

20

1778 "You should have let me know about his double game a long time ago", writes Leopold to Wolfgang. He is talking about Baron Grimm whom he considered the best Parisian mentor for his son and whose conduct, suspect at the least, has deeply disappointed him.

8

9

10

11

12

13

14

15

16

17

18

19

20

1770 Arriving in Milan on 18 October with his father, Wolfgang is not allowed any amusement for he must finish *Mitridate re del Ponto*. "I cannot write very much," he said to his mother, "for my fingers hurt because of writing all these recitatives."

Manuscript for "Ascanio in Alba" (shepherd's choir). First performed in Milan in August 1771, this opera had a very brisk success, as confirmed by the many repeats.

17 October 1771, first performance of "Ascanio in Alba" (K 111) on the occasion of the marriage of Archduke Ferdinand to the Princess of Modena, Maria Beatrice of Este. In letters sent to his wife in Salzburg, on 19 and 26 October, Leopold shows his pleasure at the tremendous success achieved by this work.

The first performance of the opera took place on the 16th [this is the *Ruggiero* by Hasse, who was also one of the first to acclaim Mozart's talent], and on the 17th, it was the *Serenata* [K 111] which achieved such a success that it is to be repeated today. The Archduke has ordered two new copies of it. Gentle men and other people from all walks of life continually hail us in the street and congratulate Wolfgang. In short ! I am so sorry but Wolfgang's *Serenata* has totally destroyed Hasse's opera, so much so that I would not know how to describe it. The success achieved by Wolfgang's *Serenata* has perhaps already circulated in Salzburg, as young Mr Kerschbaumer, who has been here for a few days, saw and heard it the day before yesterday, on the 24th. Because of the applause, Their Royal Highnesses the Archduke and Archduchess, not only had two arias repeated, but they also leaned towards Wolfgang during the *Serenata* and especially at the end of it, and expressed their pleasure to him by applauding and crying *Bravissimo Maestro*. The nobility and the whole audience were then united in applause. The opera is being performed today, yesterday there was nothing because it was Friday. Tomorrow and the day after, hence Sunday and Monday, the Serenata will be given again.

M	T	W	T	F	S	S
	1	2	3	4	5	6
7	8	9	10	11	12	13
14	15	16	17	18	19	20
21	22	23	24	25	26	27
28	29	30	31			

OCTOBER 43th WEEK

21 Monday
8
9
10
11
12
13
14
15
16
17
18
19
20

1762 Wolfgang has scarlet fever. Obliged to put off his sightseeing in Vienna, Leopold is very disappointed.

22 Tuesday
8
9
10
11
12
13
14
15
16
17
18
19
20

1777 In Augsburg, Mozart plays his *Concerto for three pianos* (written in February 1776 for Countess Lodron) with Stein the piano-maker and with the organist from the Demler Cathedral. He will reduce it to two pianos.

23 Wednesday
8
9
10
11
12
13
14
15
16
17
18
19
20

1790 Returning from Frankfurt, Mozart makes a brief stop in Mannheim, where they are preparing to stage *The Marriage*.

24 Thursday
8
9
10
11
12
13
14
15
16
17
18
19
20

1772 Obtaining a leave of absence from the Prince Archbishop of Salzburg, Leopold and Wolfgang undertake their third visit to Italy.

25 Friday
8
9
10
11
12
13
14
15
16
17
18
19
20

1777 Augsburg. Fond farewells from Wolfgang to his friendly girl cousin. He has to leave the morning after with his mother for Mannheim.

26 Saturday

8

9

10

11

12

13

14

15

16

17

18

19

20

1767 The Mozarts fled a Vienna ravaged by a terrible epidemic of smallpox without giving a single concert. Too late for Mozart however to escape the disease.

27 Sunday

8

9

10

11

12

13

14

15

16

17

18

19

20

1783 Wolfgang and Constance leave Salzburg, after fulfilling family obligations by visiting Leopold and Nannerl. Mozart will never see his birthplace again.

"Mozart at the spinet", by Joseph Duplessis, who will also paint Gluck's portrait.

26 October 1767, Wolfgang has smallpox. When he is cured, Leopold will recall his worries in his letter to Hangenauer on 10 November.

Towards ten o'clock, Wolfgang was complaining his eyes hurt; but I noticed that his head was hot, his cheeks red and burning [...] After mass, I visited His Excellency the Count von Podstatsky who received me very amicably; and when I told him my little one was sick and that I feared he had the smallpox, he told me that he wished to offer us hospitality in his home as he was not afraid of it. [...] At 4 o'clock in the afternoon, we bundled Wolfgang in sheets, leather blankets and furs and transported him in the carriage. On the 29th, we saw a few small red spots, but we still doubted it was the smallpox, as he was not getting any worse, and every 6 hours he took a potion [...]. On the 30th and 31st, his name day, he came out in a rash.

M	T	W	T	F	S	S
	1	2	3	4	5	6
7	8	9	10	11	12	13
14	15	16	17	18	19	20
21	22	23	24	25	26	27
28	29	30	31			

OCTOBER — 44th WEEK

NOVEMBER

28 Monday
8
9
10
11
12
13
14
15
16
17
18
19
20

1772 During a stop in Botzen, Mozart composes his second quartet, to pass the time.

29 Tuesday
8
9
10
11
12
13
14
15
16
17
18
19
20

1781 First night of *Don Giovanni* in Prague. Mozart wrote the overture during the preceding night. The enthusiasm of the public did not falter the whole way through the performance.

30 Wednesday
8
9
10
11
12
13
14
15
16
17
18
19
20

1762 Wolfgang has a relapse of the scarlet fever in Vienna. "Happiness is like glass", writes Leopold, who continues: "We have just broken the vinegar jug. I was only thinking we had been too happy for fourteen days; now God has sent us a small trial, and we thank him for his infinite kindness for he is already getting better."

31 Thursday
8
9
10
11
12
13
14
15
16
17
18
19
20

1762 Little Wolfgang receives a music book with 126 different pieces from his father for his name day to help him make progress.

1 Friday
8
9
10
11
12
13
14
15
16
17
18
19
20

1777 Only just arrived in Mannheim, Wolfgang is adopted by the top musicians, led by Cannabich who still brilliantly maintains the school founded by Johann Stamitz. He breathes in an atmosphere of freedom and activity totally unknown in Salzburg or even in Vienna.

2 Saturday	**3** Sunday
8	8
9	9
10	10
11	11
12	12
13	13
14	14
15	15
16	16
17	17
18	18
19	19
20	20

1778 Yielding to his father's insistency, Wolfgang leaves Strasbourg, but instead of making directly for Salzburg, he stops first in Mannheim.

1769 The success obtained by the *La finta semplice* in Salzburg has strengthened Leopold's conviction: The surest way to achieve glory is through opera. So Wolfgang must go and study the secrets of this art at source, hence in Italy. Thus he requests leave of absence from Strattenbach.

The original score for "Don Giovanni", first performed in Prague on 29 October 1787. This had a success almost as dazzling as "The Marriage", but the difficult years for Mozart were already beginning, when he would have to fight against both poverty and sickness, would find it more and more difficult to command the attention of the fickle Viennese public. And soon Joseph II, who was always well disposed towards him, would die. His successor Leopold II will on the contrary be hostile to him and will not spare him any rebuffs nor humiliation.

29 October 1787, first performance of "Don Giovanni" (K 527) in Prague. There is an unprecedented triumph for "The Marriage of Figaro", whose most famous arias were performed at street corners and during popular balls, which led to a new commission for Mozart. The opera would not be staged in Vienna until the following year, after much prevarication from the censor. Great music lover Joseph II had the work performed and had declared: "This is not the bread for Viennese teeth". To which Mozart had replied: "Well then, give them time to chew it!" On 4 November 1787, Mozart writes to his friend Gottfried von Jacquin in Vienna to share his joy with him.

I hope that you will have received my letter; on 29 October my opera *Don Giovanni* was staged, ans had the most splendid success - yesterday, it was staged for the fourth time (for my profit). I am thinking of leaving on the 12th or 13th; immediately I return you will have the aria that you want to sing [K 621 a]; *N.B.* between ourselves: I should like my good friends (Bridi and yourself especially) to be here just for one evening to share in my good fortune ! Maybe it will be arranged for Vienna ? I should like that. They are working hard here to persuade me to stay a few more months and write a new opera - but I cannot accept this offer, flattering though it may be.

Salzburg
The Only Object of his Resentment

Mozart detested Salzburg. And yet, without his being aware of it, the ravishing Baroque city, of very ancient culture, contributed to the formation of his genius. But it would have doubtlessly destroyed it if he had not revolted. «I live in a country where music has very little chance», he wrote in 1776 to the good Father Martini. It has a better chance today. Following a tradition which goes back to the end of the last century, jet setters and uppers crust receive the Mozart sacrament every season by the side of the Salzach Lake, with the cream of summer tourism in a transitory love of music and an enduring misunderstanding, on the site where Johannes Chrisostomus Wolfgang Gottlieb Mozart came into the world, one 27 January at 8 o'clock in the evening. Salzburg began to honour Mozart long after the world had already rendered him homage. Since 1783, they had ignored each other mutually. Leopold died there in 1787, Nannerl died there in 1829, but Schubert, who visited Salzburg in 1825, did not seem to know that Mozart was born there! In a long letter to his brother, he described the city and its surroundings, stopped before the house of Paracelsus and the tomb of Michael Haydn, but never mentioned Mozart who, in spirit, is associated with Vienna, not Salzburg... It was not until 1856, the year of the Centenary, that Salzburgers rediscovered their most illustrious fellow citizen, on the occasion of a performance of *Don Giovanni*. In 1870, the Mozarteum was inaugurated. Mozart's antipathy to his native city was crystallized against his sovereign and patron, Prince Archbishop Colloredo. This prelate, who succeeded in transforming Mozart's antipathy into hatred, was not the narrow-minded autocrat so frequently depicted. But he was haught and authoritarian, more interested in architecture than music, and his concept of the liturgy, compensating for the richness of ornament with a simplification of the musical contribution, could not accord with that of Mozart. Mozart could not understand that they were both, in many aspects of their personalities, men of the Enlightenment. In architecture, the modernism of which Colloredo was so proud, was Baroque, the very musical Austrian Baroque of Fischer von Erlach and Hildebrandt. There could have been a point of common agreement there;

View of Salzburg. In Mozart's time, the city prided itself on its status as an independent state governed by a prince Archbishop. Nevertheless, a narrow-mindedness of spirit, a conservatism, a sort of provincial chilliness, reigned there, which weighed heavily on a spirit as conformist as Leopold's. And even more strongly on Wolfgang's.

but neither one of them could conceive of that. The source of greatest incomprehension was not the musical indifference of the prelate, or the rigour of his reformist religious convictions (Mozart's were traditionalist); it lay mainly in the quality of the human relationship. Believing from his very early youth that a man should be valued for his talent as much as for his power, Mozart could not tolerate the haughty contempt of the Archbishop, any more than he has tolerated, at the age of eight, Mme. de Pompadour's refusal to kiss him.

Wolfgang would spend nine years in the Colloredo's service, fuming with impatience. When he resigned in May 1781, during a stay in Vienna of the archiepiscopal and princely houselhold, Mozart changed the career of musician into a liberal profession. The famous «kick in the ass» of 8 June 1781, administered by Count Arco, was a capital event in the history of music: henceforward, composers were to be solely responsible for their art. From the point of view of Mozartian creation, the Missa in C minor, performed 25 August 1783 in the attractive Church of St. ºPeter's, has been the most precious masterpiece ever offered to us by Salzburg. Constance, of whose familiar and Salzburger investiture it was, in a sense, evidence, sang

CAV. AMADEO WOLFGANGO MOZART ACCAD·FILARMON: DI BOLOG E DI VERONA

one of the soprano parts. Upon arriving at the song of the angels in the ineffable *Et incarnatus est*, Mozart celebrated his liberty, his love, and his double liberation from the authority of the Archbishop, and from that of his father.

ROLAND DE CANDE

Above, this portrait of Mozart dates from 1777. It carries the insignia of Knight of the Order of the Golden Spur.

M	T	W	T	F	S	S
				1	2	3
4	5	6	7	8	9	10
11	12	13	14	15	16	17
18	19	20	21	22	23	24
25	26	27	28	29	30	

NOVEMBER 45th WEEK

4 Monday

8
9
10
11
12
13
14
15
16
17
18
19
20

1772 Wolfgang arrives in Milan with the recitatives for *Lucio Silla* and discovers that the libretto has been changed.

5 Tuesday

8
9
10
11
12
13
14
15
16
17
18
19
20

1780 Mozart leaves Salzburg for Munich where Charles Theodore has commissioned an *opera seria* for the carnival from him. The libretto from Father Varesco for this *Idomeneo* is inspired by a Crébillon tragedy.

6 Wednesday

8
9
10
11
12
13
14
15
16
17
18
19
20

1777 Mannheim seemed to be home to a Germanic cultural renaissance, but when Mozart requests a commission for an opera in German from the Prince Elector, he is made to wait a good month before he is finally given a polite refusal.

7 Thursday

8
9
10
11
12
13
14
15
16
17
18
19
20

1790 Three days after his arrival in Vienna, where he discov ers the new home arranged by Constance (after receiving some money, she has paid the most pressing debts and recuperated the furniture), Mozart receives an offer from the Director of the Italian Opera in London. But he is not guaranteed sufficient fixed income to meet his needs, also he does not wish to give up his job at the court, which at least ensures him a regular salary. Haydn will leave in his place.

8 Friday

8
9
10
11
12
13
14
15
16
17
18
19
20

1777 Seduced by the young singer Augusta Wendling, called Gusti (daughter of the famous flautist, she is the mistress of Charles Theodore after being Johann Christian Bach's), Mozart dedicated an arietta in French to her: *Oiseaux, si tous les ans...*

1791 Once more Mozart interrupts his *Requiem* to write a masonic cantata, In *praise of friendship*, that he will conduct a few days later before his brothers in the Crown of Hope Lodge.

1781 Wolfgang to his father on the occasion of his name day: "I wish you everything that can be wished. But no, I do not wish you anything, but everything to me... since all that contributes to the happiness of your son must very naturally be acceptable to you."

View of Linz and its castle in the 18th century. Mozart stayed there for a time with Constance when they were on their way back from Salzburg, and this was where he composed the "Linz" Symphony. These were also particularly fruitful years, more so than those following their wedding and during which the quartets dedicated to Haydn and the great concertos (K 449, 450, 451, 456 and 459) were born.

In 1783, Wolfgang and Constance visited Salzburg, wishing to make their peace with Leopold, who will greet the young woman very coolly, as does Nannerl. The couple will stop at Linz on the way back, where they will receive the cordial hospitality of Count Thun, the father of their faithful Viennese patron. Wishing to thank his hosts appropriately, Mozart decides to dedicate a composition to them. He writes a symphony in a few days: this will be the "Linz Symphony", first performed on 4 November 1783. When he wrote to his father on 31 October, the work was not yet completed.

Count Thun (brother of the Vienna Thun) came to see me straightaway and told me that his father had already been expecting me for two weeks, that I was to have myself driven directly to his home where I was to be lodged. The day after, when we were at the gateway to Linz, a manservant was waiting for us to take us to the old Count Thun where we are now lodging. I could not begin to tell you of the overwhelming kindness we have received in this house. Tuesday, 4 November, I am giving a concert at the theatre here - and as I do not have a single symphony in my luggage, I am hurriedly writing a new one which will have to be finished by this date.

M	T	W	T	F	S	S
				1	2	3
4	5	6	7	8	9	10
11	12	13	14	15	16	17
18	19	20	21	22	23	24
25	26	27	28	29	30	

NOVEMBER 46th WEEK

11 Monday
8
9
10
11
12
13
14
15
16
17
18
19
20

1778 The return to Mannheim gives Mozart the feeling of celebration: "My being is literally uprooted."

12 Tuesday
8
9
10
11
12
13
14
15
16
17
18
19
20

1778 Baron Dalberg, author of a libretto, asks Gluck, Schweitzer and Mozart for the score, but Mozart chooses instead to put Voltaire's *Sémiramis* to music. But he will leave Mannheim before completing this project.

13 Wednesday
8
9
10
11
12
13
14
15
16
17
18
19
20

1777 One year earlier in Mannheim. Confronted with delays at court, Mozart's situation becomes precarious and he has to contract a loan.

14 Thursday
8
9
10
11
12
13
14
15
16
17
18
19
20

1765 After Nannerl, now Wolfgang falls ill in The Hague. One week in a semi-comatose state leaves him practically exhausted. Leopold increases the masses for the acts of grace so that the Lord on High might spare his assets in his progeny.

15 Friday
8
9
10
11
12
13
14
15
16
17
18
19
20

1786 Scarcely one month old, little Johann Thomas dies. Mozart, who had written to his father to ask him to temporarily take charge of his children - on payment of an allowance - so he can undertake a new tour of England with Constance, receives a rather dry refusal a few days later.

16 Saturday

0

1

2

3

4

5

6

7

8

9

0

1789 Joseph II has commissioned a new work for the Italian Opera of Vienna and for this, it is said, would have himself chosen the subject and title: *Cosi fan tutte*. However, Wolfgang's joy is overshadowed by the loss of his last child, little Anna, who has lived only a few hours.

17 Sunday

8

9

10

11

12

13

14

15

16

17

18

19

20

1765 The Mozarts arrive in Paris and descend upon Count Van Eyck, the Bavarian Ambassador.

Verſuch einer gründlichen Violinſchule,

entworfen

und mit 4. Kupfertafeln ſammt einer Tabelle verſehen

von

Leopold Mozart

Hochfürſtl. Salzburgiſchen Cammermuſikus.

In Verlag des Verfaſſers.

Augſpurg,
gedruckt bey Johann Jacob Letter, 1756.

A treatise on the violin published by Leopold Mozart in 1756. Excellent violinist and quite a respected, even inspired composer, Wolfgang's father was a terrible writer with both an exaggerated and clumsy style. However he did not lack shrewdness and was able to understand that the petty and provincial atmosphere of Salzburg risked strangling the genius of his son. Thus he gave Wolfgang a glittering and cosmopolitan education.

14 November 1719, birth of Leopold Mozart. - 5 November, Saint Leopold's day. 8 November 1777 Mozart sends his wishes to his father.

Dear Father!

I cannot write poetically, I am not a poet. I would not know how to arrange the phrases artistically enough to make the shadows and lights dance, I am not a painter. Nor can I express my feelings and my thoughts by gesture and through the *Pantomime*, I am not a dancer. But thanks to sound I can do it, I am a Musikus. Tomorrow, I will play the piano at Cannabich's, in your honour with all my best wishes for your name day and birthday. Today I can only wish you with all my heart, my dear Father, everyhing that I wish for you every day, morning and evening -health, long life and good temper. I also hope that you have less worry now than when I was still in Salzburg, as I must admit to have been its sole cause. I was badly treated and did not deserve it; naturally you were sympathetic, but not overly. [...] Now I must conclude with a musical wish. I wish you to live as many years as it is necessary to no longer be in a position to compose anything new. [...] I kiss the hands of Papa 1000 times and remain until death

My dear Father
Your obedient son
Wolfgang Amadeus Mozart

M	T	W	T	F	S	S
				1	2	3
4	5	6	7	8	9	10
11	12	13	14	15	16	17
18	19	20	21	22	23	24
25	26	27	28	29	30	

NOVEMBER 47ᵗʰ WEEK

22 Friday

21 Thursday

20 Wednesday

19 Tuesday

18 Monday

1771 In Milan, Leopold asks the Archduke Charles Ferdinand for a position at court for his son.

1778 Leopold summons Wolfgang to return to Salzburg, listing for him all the debts contracted in the interest of his career.

1791 Vienna. Mozart has to be confined to bed. Constance sends for the doctor. That evening, the 100th is stuck on the poster for *The Magic Flute* at the Auf der Wieden Theatre.

1785 Da Ponte extracted a promise from Joseph II to stage *The Marriage* in Vienna, which does not prevent Mozart from being obliged to appeal to Hofmeister to try and resolve his financial problems.

1780 Wolfgang sends Leopold a letter from Munich which he finishes in this way: "My compliments to all my good friends, men and women, Without forgetting that bum Katherl Gilowsky; give Pimperl [the Mozarts' dog] a whiff of Spanish tobacco, a good mash with wine and three kisses."

8	
9	
10	
11	
12	
13	
14	
15	
16	
17	
18	
19	
20	

1781 Wolfgang in Vienna: "The Grand Duke [of Russia], that strange beast, is here. Tomorrow the *Alceste* (by Gluck) is being given in Italian at Schönbrunn. And then a free ball. I have made enquiries for favourite Russian songs to make variations on them."

1778 Ultimatum from Leopold demanding his son leave Mannheim by first coach.

23 November 1781: Mozart gives a concert at the home of his pupil Josepha Barbara Auernhammer. Letter to his father dated 24 November.

Yesterday I was at a a concert at the Auernhammer's when Ceccarelli brought the letter; so he did not find me and hence left the letter with the Webers [...] Present at the concert were Countess Thun (whom I had invited), Baron van Swieten, Baron Gudenus, the rich Jew baptised Wetzlar, Count Firmian and Mr von Daubrawaick and his son. We played the *Concerto* for two pianos and a Sonata for two pianos [K 365 and K 448] that I composed expressly for this event, and which had a great success. I will have this sonata sent by Mr von Daubrawaick who said that he would be proud to carry it in his case; it was the son who said this, and *nota bene* a man of Salzburg. But after the departure of his father, he said very loudly - I am proud to be your compatriot; you are bringing great honour to Salzburg. I do hope that the times will change so that we could have you back. And then we would certainly not let you go again. To which I replied - My birthplace still has first call on me.

18 November 1791: Mozart directs his "Masonic Cantata" for the inauguration of the newly crowned Hope Lodge. On 20 November 1791, he is confined to bed never to get up again.

The last Viennese residence of the Mozart couple, in Raubes teibgasse. This is where Mozart died.

M	T	W	T	F	S	S
				1	2	3
4	5	6	7	8	9	10
11	12	13	14	15	16	17
18	19	20	21	22	23	24
25	26	27	28	29	30	

NOVEMBER 48th WEEK

25 Monday
8
9
10
11
12
13
14
15
16
17
18
19
20

1780 Leopold to his son: "Dress warmly, do not drink wine [...]. Drink tea for breakfast ..."

26 Tuesday
8
9
10
11
12
13
14
15
16
17
18
19
20

1778 His creative flow stemmed, Wolfgang will write practically nothing until the following spring. He re-orchestrates some Handel oratorios for van Swieten.

27 Wednesday
8
9
10
11
12
13
14
15
16
17
18
19
20

1764 In London, Wolfgang completes the six sonatas for harpsichord with violin accompaniment which will appear two months later, dedicated to Queen Sophie Charlotte.

28 Thursday
8
9
10
11
12
13
14
15
16
17
18
19
20

1791 Wolfgang's condition has deteriorated. The doctor in charge of the hospital thinks it is hopeless.

29 Friday
8
9
10
11
12
13
14
15
16
17
18
19
20

1777 Wolfgang receives a letter in Mannheim in which Leopold reproaches him for this too lengthy and unfruitful stay. Three days later, a further scolding.

1 Sunday

8

30 Saturday

9

10

11

12

13

14

15

16

17

18

19

20

1780 Nannerl tells her brother about the first night in Salzburg of a Schikaneder play: "The Archbishop left during the third act and the public in batches a few at a time... When it was all over, the people applauded, whistled, tapped their canes and cried for a [encore] in mockery."

1763 Grimm in his *Correspondance littéraire* publishes an article which opens the doors of the Paris salons to the young Mozarts.

Baron Grimm, who gave very effective publicity to the Mozart children.

On 1 December, Baron Grimm devotes an article in his "Correspondance littéraire" to the Mozart children.

True prodigies are rare indeed so that when you have the opportunity of seeing one, you talk about it. A choirmaster from Salzburg, called Mozart, has just arrived here with two children with the prettiest faces in the world. His daughter, aged eleven years, plays the harpsichord so brilliantly; she performs the greatest and most difficult pieces with a surprising accuracy. Her brother, who will be seven years old next February, is such an extraordinary phenomenon that what you see with your own eyes and hear with your own ears is scarcely believable. It is not much for this child to perform the most difficult of pieces with the greatest precision with hands that can hardly reach the sixth; what is incredible is to see him play from memory for an hour at a time, and then abandons himself in his inspired genius and in a host of entrancing ideas that he can still make one after another follow with refinement and without confusion. The most learned choirmaster would not know how to delve deeper than he into the science of harmony and modulations that he can lead along the least known, but always correct roads. He has such a great skill on the piano that when it is concealed from him by a unfolded napkin, he plays on top of the napkin with the same speed and precision. It is easy for him to play all the music presented to him; he writes and composes with marvellous ease, without needing to be close to the harpsichord.

Vienna
Disillusionment at Twilight

The ten years that Mozart spent in Vienna were a series of decrescendos after a crescendo and a climax (*Le Nozze di Figaro*, 1786). At first, all his dreams seemed to be coming true: he married Constance Weber, with whom he was passionately in love, although his father only reluctantly gave his consent; the visit to Salzburg in 1783 to present Constance to his father and sister was far from a success.

Nevertheless, musically, his career was flourishing, and his subscription concerts were not only an artistic success, but a financial one. Leopold Mozart, upon a visit to his son and family in 1785, saw that the appartment he occupied, large and expensive, was like a beehive, intense and happy. The family often received guests, and was received no less often. Since Wolfgang had become a Freemason, he persuaded his father to request his admission onto the brotherhood, which had already attracted a large number of brilliant men. The following year, Mozart composed *Le Nozze di Figaro*, which enjoyed a certain

success, particularly upon its performance in Prague. Although the visit of the Mozarts to Prague in 1787 represented a great financial success, and opened the door for the commission for *Don Giovanni*, the extravagant life style that Mozart led was beginning to exceed his means. It was, therefore, with relief that he learned that the Emperor, Joseph II, had decided to grant him a modest title (Kamermusicus), accompanied by a moderate

salary of 800 guilders per year. The five last years of Mozart's life saw him gradually deluged in debt: what was, however, more striking was that his subscription concerts were being poorly attended, and it was no longer fashionable to listen to his piano. Mozart's public concerts, not very frequent, were becoming non-existent, and his financial situation was becoming extremely critical, due to the constant illnesses of his wife, the result of her many

pregnancies; it was even necessary for her to take an expensive cure at Baden. Finally, the situation became desesperate and, at the time of his death, on 5 December 1791, Mozart was riddled with debt. Why did Mozart choose to remain in a city that did not appreciate him? What were the alternatives? Apparently, he had two important offers before him to work in as many different European capitals, London and Berlin, but he declined both of them. Mozart had perfectly sound reasons for not wishing to budge from Vienna. He did not want to risk his nomination at the court, which was a source of regular if not significant income for him. But there were just as many artistic factors: the court Opera was one of the best in Europe, and included Italian virtuoso singers; its reputation was international. In the same manner, the orchestra to which Mozart had entrusted for his subscription concerts, was without doubt one of the best in the world, and absolutely without peer in the woodwinds and horns. Ecclesiastical music had reached the highest pinnacle in all of Catholic Europe, supported there by two principal institutions, the St. Stephen's Cathedral and the Hofmusikkapelle (Chapel of the Royal and Imperial Court).

Below, this earthenware tile manufactured in Lille with the «Magic Flute» motif (end of the 18th century), testifies to the popularity of this opera, created 30 September 1791.

Other churches also maintained musical organizations of the first rank. The accession of Leopold II to the throne had permitted the employment of a sufficient number of musicians by the churches, his predecessor Joseph II having forbidden or considerably diminished them. But the principal factor which induced Mozart to remain in Vienna was that he had been given the promise, with the position to follow, of the post of Kapellmeister at the St. Stephen's Cathedral, upon the death of its occupant —the old Leopold Hofmann— which occured in 1793. Mozart would then have had a very comfortable salary of 2,000 guilders per year, plus other advantages in kind (firewood, candles, etc.). This was something to dream about. Upon his death, Leopold Hofman was one of the richest composers in the whole history of Vienna, between Haydn and Raimund. Mozart considered —naturally— that he could aspire to such heights, once the coveted position had been attained. He thus hoped to avoid the courtesan intrigues of Salieri's opera by moving to the suburbs, and by composing operas in the German language; in this, he was not mistaken: his new German opera, *The Magic Flute*, was destined to be the greatest

success of his career and to conquer all of Germanic Europe. It is certain that Schikaneder and Mozart would not have stopped there. Finally, let us add a truism: Vienna was an intensely musical city, in which everyone, from the Emperor to the ladies' maids, was in some way bound up with composition or performance. That was certainly not the case in Berlin or London, whence Mozart had received his concrete proposals, (Paris in 1791 being prone to other upheavals). Vienna had such a hold on Mozart simply because in the long run, he preferred it to all other cities open to him. People who don't like Vienna, and there are a few, will never understand the reasons why he declined the offers from London and Berlin. But people for whom Vienna still has a magic, for whom it is a place of extraordinary fascination, will easily understand the exclusive devotion and love that Mozart felt for this charming (though not always quite faithful) city.

R.C. ROBBINS-LANDON

Above left, Antonio Salieri. Mozart's glory seemed to put him in the shade, and he never ceased to plot cabals against him. But he was not the mysterious «man in black» as has long been claimed. On the right, the unfinished portrait of the composer by his brother-in-law, Lange, Aloysia's husband. Below, the Cholmarkt in Vienna, by Carl Schutz (detail).

	M	T	W	T	F	S	S
							1
	2	3	4	5	6	7	8
	9	10	11	12	13	14	15
	16	17	18	19	20	21	22
	23	24	25	26	27	28	29
	30	31					

DECEMBER   49th WEEK

2 Monday

8

9

10

11

12

13

14

15

16

17

18

19

20

1779 Salzburg. Mozart transforms *La finta giardiniera* into a singspiel for Boehm's travelling company.

3 Tuesday

8

9

10

11

12

13

14

15

16

17

18

19

20

1791 In his bedroom, Mozart organises a rehearsal of fragments of the *Requiem*. The priests from Saint Peter's refuse to give the last rites to a Freemason.

4 Wednesday

8

9

10

11

12

13

14

15

16

17

18

19

20

1786 Vienna. Mozart completes his twenty-fifth concerto for piano (K 503).

5 Thursday

8

9

10

11

12

13

14

15

16

17

18

19

20

1791 Mozart passes away at 0 h 55.

6 Friday

8

9

10

11

12

13

14

15

16

17

18

19

20

1791 After a short service in Saint Stephen's Cathedral, a third class funeral procession accompanies Mozart to the communal grave at the Saint Marx cemetery, outside the ramparts. Constance, close to a nervous breakdown, does not attend the ceremony.

7 Saturday

8 Sunday

8	8
9	9
10	10
11	11
12	12
13	13
14	14
15	15
16	16
17	17
18	18
19	19
20	20

1774 Leopold and his son arrive in Munich where the Elector of Bavaria, Maximilian III, has commissioned *La finta giardiniera* from him.

1787 Three weeks after Gluck passes away, Joseph II confers the title of Composer to the Imperial and Royal Chamber upon Mozart, but with an appreciably lower remuneration.

"The Funeral of Mozart". There are several variations in the form of engravings of this anonymous picture. For the romantic, Mozart was personification itself of the accursed artist, the misunderstood genius.

5 December 1791, 5 minutes to 1 in the morning: death of Wolfgang Amadeus Mozart. His widow Constance, the same day writes this note on the visitors' book in which he had expressed his own sorrow at the death of his friend Barisani.
"What you wrote before concerning your friend,
"I repeat it for you here, as I bow under the grief.
"Darling husband! A Mozart immortal to me and all Europe
"You as well, now you are at peace - for ever!
"1 hour after midnight, on the night of 4 to 5 December this year,
"In his 36th year - too soon, oh much too soon! He left.
"This world good certainly - but ungrateful! Oh God !
"eight years unite us in an affectionate and indelible bond !
"Oh, that I may soon be united with you for ever.
Your grief-stricken wife
Constance Mozart née Weber

6 December 1791, Mozart is buried in the Saint Marx cemetery in Vienna. The diary of Count Zinzendorf proves that the supposed snow storm of this day is an embellishment to the legend:
"Mild weather. And frequent fog."

M	T	W	T	F	S	S
						1
2	3	4	5	6	7	8
9	10	11	12	13	14	15
16	17	18	19	20	21	22
23	24	25	26	27	28	29
30	31					

DECEMBER   50ᵗʰ WEEK

9 Monday

8
9
10
11
12
13
14
15
16
17
18
19
20

1778 Mozart leaves Mannheim, abandoning all his plans, including the writing of a German opera.

10 Tuesday

8
9
10
11
12
13
14
15
16
17
18
19
20

1769 Leopold and Wolfgang prepare to leave for Innsbruck, first stop on their journey to Italy.

11 Wednesday

8
9
10
11
12
13
14
15
16
17
18
19
20

1780 To Leopold who advises him to write for the public at large, Wolfgang retorts that with *Idomeneo* there will be music for everyone, "without forgetting those with long ears".

12 Thursday

8
9
10
11
12
13
14
15
16
17
18
19
20

1780 Mozart is working on Zaide (probably from Voltaire's play) for Boehm. But the death of Maria Theresa causes the theatres to be closed and compromises this project, so the work remained unfinished.

13 Friday

8
9
10
11
12
13
14
15
16
17
18
19
20

1790 Set free by the death of Prince Esterhazy, Haydn prepares to leave Vienna for London. Mozart will spend the day of the 14th with him, repeating continually through his tears: "I fear, Papa, that we are seeing one another for the last time."

14 Saturday

8

9

10

11

12

13

14

15

16

17

18

19

20

1784 Mozart belongs to the Freemasons and is initiated into the rank of apprentice at the Benevolence Lodge under the presidency of his old friend Gemmingen. Less than four months later, he will rise to the rank of master.

15 Sunday

8

9

10

11

12

13

14

15

16

17

18

19

20

1781 In a letter to Leopold, Wolfgang reveals his passion for Constance, the young sister of Aloysia Weber.

In the 18th century these "silhouettes" are the fashion; that of Mozart is well known.

13 December 1769. Leopold and Wolfgang leave for their first trip to Italy. As soon as the day after, Mozart, writing to his mother and sister still in Salzburg, shows his pleasure for travel.

My darling Mama, My heart is absolutely full of joy because this journey is so amusing and it is so warm in the carriage, and because our coachman is a courteous boy who drives very fast as soon as the road at all allows.

Wolfgang Mozart

Carissima sorella mia, We have, thank God, arrived safely in Wörgl. I must say that it is very amusing to travel, it is absolutely not cold and that our carriage is as warm as a bedroom. [...] Keep your spirits up, *addio.*

Wolfgang Mozart

M	T	W	T	F	S	S
						1
2	3	4	5	6	7	8
9	10	11	12	13	14	15
16	17	18	19	20	21	22
23	24	25	26	27	28	29
30	31					

DECEMBER 51th WEEK

20 Friday
8
9
10
11
12
13
14
15
16
17
18
19
20

1775 Salzburg. *Fifth violin concerto* K 219.

19 Thursday
8
9
10
11
12
13
14
15
16
17
18
19
20

1772 The rehearsals for *Lucio Silla* begin in Milan. First performed on the 26th, the work would only be moderately suc cessful after narrowly avoiding catastrophe on the first night.

18 Wednesday
8
9
10
11
12
13
14
15
16
17
18
19
20

1778 On the way to Munich, Mozart is nostalgic for Mannheim: "I have never had so much heart-felt pain before on leaving, the journey has only been half-way pleasant. It would not have been so at all, and would have even been tiresome, if I had not been accustomed since childhood to leave people, towns and countries."

17 Tuesday
8
9
10
11
12
13
14
15
16
17
18
19
20

1777 In spite of Charles Theodore's refusal which deprives him of all hope of obtaining a position at court, Mozart decides to spend the winter in Mannheim. He obtains board and lodging in return for lessons.

16 Monday
8
9
10
11
12
13
14
15
16
17
18
19
20

1771 Arriving home from Italy, Leopold and Wolfgang reach Salzburg on the day of Strattenbach's death.

21 Saturday	22 Sunday
8	8
9	9
10	10
11	11
12	12
13	13
14	14
15	15
16	16
17	17
18	18
19	19
20	20

1777 Mozart becomes acquainted with Wieland, who has come to Mannheim to watch over the finishing touches to *Rosamunde* in which he has a part of the libretto: "The reality was different from what I had visualised. He seemed rather affected in his speech, he has a voice similar to that of a child, a cer tain way of inspecting you which is close to contrived impoliteness... His face is comfortingly ugly, covered with marks from smallpox, and he has a fairly long nose."

1780 Leopold writes to his son regarding cuts to *Idomeneo:* "At rehearsal when the eye has nothing to look at, of course you may become bored, but in the theatre where there are so many sources of distraction, between the stage-set itself and the other spectators, such a recitative passes unnoticed."

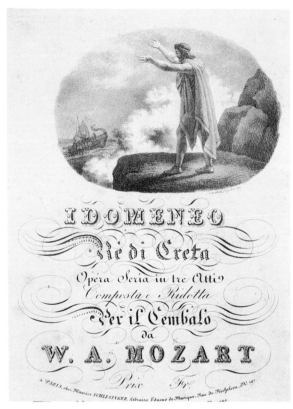

Frontispiece from the score of "Idomeneo", opera first performed in Munich on 20 January 1781.

16 December 1780, rehearsal for "Idomeneo" (K 366) at the court in Munich. Mozart's letter to his father, 19 December.

I have indeed received the latest aria for Raaf [Anton Raaf, performing the rôle of *Idomeneo*], who sends you his compliments, the trumpet mutes, your latest letter dated the 15th and the pair of understockings. The last rehearsal, just like the first, went off very well - the orchestra and the whole audience were pleased to note that they were mistaken in thinking that the second act could not surpass the first in expression and originality; next Saturday, we will rehearse again but in a large hall at court, what we have been wanting for a long time, for it is too little at Count Seeau's. The Prince Elector [Charles Theodore of the Bavarian Palatinate] will listen *(incognito)* in an adjoining room - but it will have to be rehearsed with body and soul, as Cannabich told me [Christian Cannabich, Director of the Orchestra]. I was bathed in sweat during the first rehearsal.

	M	T	W	T	F	S	S
							1
	2	3	4	5	6	7	8
	9	10	11	12	13	14	15
	16	17	18	19	20	21	22
	23	24	25	26	27	28	29
	30	31					

DECEMBER 52th WEEK

27 Friday

8

9

10

11

12

13

14

15

16

17

18

19

20

1787 Constance brings her fourth child into the world, a daughter called Theresa. Once more the Mozarts have moved house to live more cheaply close to Graben.

26 Thursday

8

9

10

11

12

13

14

15

16

17

18

19

20

1770 Milan. The first night of *Mitriddate re di Ponto* is a success. The impressario Castiglione thus proposes that Mozart open the 1772-1773 season.

25 Wednesday

8

9

10

11

12

13

14

15

16

17

18

19

20

1778 Wolfgang arrives in Munich where he is to offer the Princess Elector his Paris Sonatas. He rushes to the Weber's to find that the beautiful Aloysia is no longer so favourably well disposed towards him. A song will avenge him for her unfaithfulness.

24 Tuesday

8

9

10

11

12

13

14

15

16

17

18

19

20

1781 Joseph II, who preferred Salieri as a teacher for Princess Elizabeth, invites Mozart to court. This will be the opportunity for a memorable confrontation at the piano with Clementi.

23 Monday

8

9

10

11

12

13

14

15

16

17

18

19

20

1781 Mozart declares he is engaged to marry Constance. He has, in fact, succumbed to pressure from Frau Weber.

29 Sunday

8

9

10

11

12

13

14

15

16

17

18

19

20

28 Saturday

8

9

10

11

12

13

14

15

16

17

18

19

20

1791 Leopold II authorises Constance to arrange a concert for the few works left by Mozart. The receipts will cover all her debts. Vienna discovers what a fine musician it has lost.

1770 Leopold and Wolfgang arrive in Verona where the local aristocracy waylays the young boy, whilst the crowd are waiting for him to play the organ which is his custom in each city he passes through.

Muzio Clementi was considered a master of the keyboard of the period.

24 December 1781, Mozart compares himself on the piano with Muzio Clementi, upon whom he gives his impressions to his father on 16 January 1782.
He is a bold harpsichordist. - But that it all. He has great agility in his right hand - his best *passages* are the thirds -, in other respects, he has neither the taste nor feeling for a kreutzer - a simple *Mechanicus.* After sufficient reciprocal *compliments,* the Emperor decided that he would be the one to begin to play La *santa Chiesa catholica,* because, he said, Clementi is a Roman. He played a prelude and then a sonata - then the Emperor said to me: *Allons,* off we go. I also played a prelude with variations. Then the Grand Duchess [Maria Feodo rovna] brought some of Paisiello's sonatas (miserably written in the latter's own hand): I had to play the *Allego,* he the *Andante* and the *Rondo.* Then we took a theme from them and developed it on two *pianos forte* - I have to say that I had borrowed the *piano forte* from Countess Thun, but I only played on it when I was alone.

M	T	W	T	F	S	S
						1
2	3	4	5	6	7	8
9	10	11	12	13	14	15
16	17	18	19	20	21	22
23	24	25	26	27	28	29
30	31					

1992   1ˢᵗ WEEK

30 Monday
8
9
10
11
12
13
14
15
16
17
18
19
20

1780 The rehearsals for *Idomeneo*, began a month ago, continue to general satisfaction.

31 Tuesday
8
9
10
11
12
13
14
15
16
17
18
19
20

1778 Anna Maria Thekla rejoins her cousin Wolfgang in Munich. She then accompanies him to Salzburg, making the return less painful.

1 Wednesday
8
9
10
11
12
13
14
15
16
17
18
19
20

2 Thursday
8
9
10
11
12
13
14
15
16
17
18
19
20

3 Friday
8
9
10
11
12
13
14
15
16
17
18
19
20

	8
	9
	10
0	11
1	12
2	13
3	14
4	15
5	16
6	17
7	18
8	19
9	20
20	

This "silhouette" would be Mozart's at the time he was working in Prague on his "Don Giovanni." Nothing gave Wolfgang more pleasure than to take to the road again, with Constance and Da Ponte, to see the people of Prague again who had given him such an enthusiastic response to the revival of "The Marriage of Figaro." They met Casanova there, who was residing at the time in a castle in the suburbs, where he was performing the job of librarian and who, perhaps, gave them a few ideas (it is at least tempting to imagine so). As soon as the work was finished, Da Ponte had to leave again for Vienna, where Salieri was waiting for him. Alone, Mozart accepted the hospitality of his faithful friend Josepha Duschek. To thank her he had promised to write her a concert aria but he kept on putting it off until the day after. Then his charming hostess had to lock him up in a little pavilion in the garden, declaring that she would not set him free until the aria was finished, and Wolfgang had to submit.

Edited by :
France - EDITIONS ATLAS s. a.
89, rue La Boétie, 75008 Paris.

Belgium - EDITIONS ATLEN s. a.
Avenue George Rodenbach 4,
1030 Brussels.

The Editors wish to express their special thanks to Mrs. Brigitte Massin for her assistance in designing this diary.

The extracts from Mozart's correspondence are taken from the monumental edition by Geneviève Geffray, currently in publication by Editions Flammarion.

The article by Jacques Lonchampt is taken from L'Opéra aujourd'hui, published by Editions du Seuil (1970).

Lay-out : Jean-Claude Bernar

Illustrations. Arch. IGDA: 21, 25, 33, 49b, 51, 57, 59a, 63, 65, 80-81, 83, 85, 89, 91b, 95a, 119, 123, 133; A Dagli Orti-Arch. IGDA: 19, 23, 27, 29, 37, 39a, 41, 43, 47, 53, 55, 60-61, 61a, 67, 69, 75, 77, 91a, 95b, 97, 99, 101, 102, 105a, 105b, 107, 109, 111, 117, 124, 127, 131, 135a, 137, 141, 143; A. De Gregorio-Arch IGDA: 45,; Bridgeman Art Library-Arch. IGDA: 48-49; A. Nimatallah-Arch. IGDA: 49a; M. Seemuller-Arch. IGDA: 102-103; E. Lessing-Arch. IGDA: 113; Explorer Archives: 38, 79; ERL-Sipa Icono: 35, 59b, 121; Edimedia: 71a; Goldner-Sipa Icono: 31; Arthephot-Mandel: 80; Giraudon: 73, 114; Lauros-Giraudon: 125, 134; Sipa Icono: 87; DR: 7, 28, 39b, 61b, 61c, 70, 71b, 81, 92, 92-93, 93, 103, 114, 115, 125c, 129, 135c, 139, 145.

© EDITIONS ATLAS, Paris, 1990.
Legal Deposit : april 1991.
Printed in France by Herissey.

The Authors

GENEVIÈVE GEFFRAY
A musicologist at the Salzburg Mozarteum, Geneviève Geffray is currently publishing the French translation of Mozart's correspondence in five volumes (Editions Flammarion) to be followed by two additional volumes, one dedicated to the correspondence of Constance Mozart, and the other to various writings related to the musician.

BRIGITTE MASSIN
A musicologist, Brigitte Massin has published authoritative biographies of Mozart and Beethoven with her husband, Jean Massin, as well as a biography of Schubert under her name alone. She is working on a biography of Schumann.

MARIE-CHRISTINE VILA
A trained academic, Marie-Christine Vila is the author of Sotto Voce, Mozart à Paris en 1778. She is also preparing a book entitled Un philosophe, un musicien, Rousseau et Mozart and is collaborating on the Guide des opéras de Mozart, currently in preparation.

PHILIPPE BEAUSSANT
A musicologist and writer, Philippe Beaussant is today one of the directors of the Baroque Music Center in Versailles.

THIERRY BEAUVERT
Thierry Beauvert is the editor of Le Monde de la musique.

ROLAND DE CANDÉ
The author of many works, one wich is entitled Histoire de la musique and another Jean-Sébastien Bach, Roland de Candé is preparing a Dictionnaire des chefs-d'œuvre de la musique.

JEAN-VICTOR HOCQUARD
Jean-Victor Hocquard has published approximately 10 works on Mozart, among them Mozart, l'amour, la mort, Ecrits et propos sur Mozart, and Mozart l'unique.

H.C. ROBBINS LANDON
A musicologist and specialist of Hayden, H.C. Robbins Landon has published notably 1792, La dernière année de Mozart, and 1781-1791, L'âge d'or de la musique à Vienne.

JACQUES LONCHAMPT
A journalist for Le Monde, Jacques Lonchampt is the author of several works, among them L'Opéra aujourd'hui.

SERGIO SEGALINI
Sergio Segalini is the editor of Opéra international.

MARC VIGNAL
A musicologist and journalist, Marc Vignal is the author of an essential work of Hayden.

JANUARY

1 ....
2 ....
3 ....
4 ....
5 ....
6 ....
7 ....
8 ....
9 ....
10 ....
11 ....
12 ....
13 ....
14 ....
15 ....
16 ....
17 ....
18 ....
19 ....
20 ....
21 ....
22 ....
23 ....
24 ....
25 ....
26 ....
27 ....
28 ....
29 ....
30 ....
31 ....

FEBRUARY

1 ....
2 ....
3 ....
4 ....
5 ....
6 ....
7 ....
8 ....
9 ....
10 ....
11 ....
12 ....
13 ....
14 ....
15 ....
16 ....
17 ....
18 ....
19 ....
20 ....
21 ....
22 ....
23 ....
24 ....
25 ....
26 ....
27 ....
28 ....
29 ....

MARCH

1 ....
2 ....
3 ....
4 ....
5 ....
6 ....
7 ....
8 ....
9 ....
10 ....
11 ....
12 ....
13 ....
14 ....
15 ....
16 ....
17 ....
18 ....
19 ....
20 ....
21 ....
22 ....
23 ....
24 ....
25 ....
26 ....
27 ....
28 ....
29 ....
30 ....
31 ....

APRIL

1 ....
2 ....
3 ....
4 ....
5 ....
6 ....
7 ....
8 ....
9 ....
10 ....
11 ....
12 ....
13 ....
14 ....
15 ....
16 ....
17 ....
18 ....
19 ....
20 ....
21 ....
22 ....
23 ....
24 ....
25 ....
26 ....
27 ....
28 ....
29 ....
30 ....

MAY

1 ....
2 ....
3 ....
4 ....
5 ....
6 ....
7 ....
8 ....
9 ....
10 ....
11 ....
12 ....
13 ....
14 ....
15 ....
16 ....
17 ....
18 ....
19 ....
20 ....
21 ....
22 ....
23 ....
24 ....
25 ....
26 ....
27 ....
28 ....
29 ....
30 ....
31 ....

JUNE

1 ....
2 ....
3 ....
4 ....
5 ....
6 ....
7 ....
8 ....
9 ....
10 ....
11 ....
12 ....
13 ....
14 ....
15 ....
16 ....
17 ....
18 ....
19 ....
20 ....
21 ....
22 ....
23 ....
24 ....
25 ....
26 ....
27 ....
28 ....
29 ....
30 ....

JULY

1 ....
2 ....
3 ....
4 ....
5 ....
6 ....
7 ....
8 ....
9 ....
10 ....
11 ....
12 ....
13 ....
14 ....
15 ....
16 ....
17 ....
18 ....
19 ....
20 ....
21 ....
22 ....
23 ....
24 ....
25 ....
26 ....
27 ....
28 ....
29 ....
30 ....
31 ....

AUGUST

1 ....
2 ....
3 ....
4 ....
5 ....
6 ....
7 ....
8 ....
9 ....
10 ....
11 ....
12 ....
13 ....
14 ....
15 ....
16 ....
17 ....
18 ....
19 ....
20 ....
21 ....
22 ....
23 ....
24 ....
25 ....
26 ....
27 ....
28 ....
29 ....
30 ....
31 ....

SEPTEMBER

1 ....
2 ....
3 ....
4 ....
5 ....
6 ....
7 ....
8 ....
9 ....
10 ....
11 ....
12 ....
13 ....
14 ....
15 ....
16 ....
17 ....
18 ....
19 ....
20 ....
21 ....
22 ....
23 ....
24 ....
25 ....
26 ....
27 ....
28 ....
29 ....
30 ....

OCTOBER

1 ....
2 ....
3 ....
4 ....
5 ....
6 ....
7 ....
8 ....
9 ....
10 ....
11 ....
12 ....
13 ....
14 ....
15 ....
16 ....
17 ....
18 ....
19 ....
20 ....
21 ....
22 ....
23 ....
24 ....
25 ....
26 ....
27 ....
28 ....
29 ....
30 ....
31 ....

NOVEMBER

1 ....
2 ....
3 ....
4 ....
5 ....
6 ....
7 ....
8 ....
9 ....
10 ....
11 ....
12 ....
13 ....
14 ....
15 ....
16 ....
17 ....
18 ....
19 ....
20 ....
21 ....
22 ....
23 ....
24 ....
25 ....
26 ....
27 ....
28 ....
29 ....
30 ....

DECEMBER

1 ....
2 ....
3 ....
4 ....
5 ....
6 ....
7 ....
8 ....
9 ....
10 ....
11 ....
12 ....
13 ....
14 ....
15 ....
16 ....
17 ....
18 ....
19 ....
20 ....
21 ....
22 ....
23 ....
24 ....
25 ....
26 ....
27 ....
28 ....
29 ....
30 ....
31 ....

ADDRESS-BOOK

A B

Name and address | ☎

C D

☏ Name and address

Name and address   ☎

G H I

☎ | Name and address

JKL

Name and address ☎

MNO

✆	Name and address

P Q R

Name and address ☎

S T

☎ | Name and address

Name and address

X Y Z

📞 | Name and address